NEVER GIVE UP

New Hope for Parkinson's Patients

A True Story by Harry Knitter

ISBN: 1-40331-290-7 (e-book)
ISBN: 1-40331-291-5 (Paperback)

This book is printed on acid free paper.

1stBooks - rev. 06/24/02

The information in this book is accurate to the best knowledge of the author and publisher. Because every medical condition is unique, however, the treatments received by the writer were specifically designed for him, and probably would work differently on other patients.

Production Credits:

Cover Layout: Jim Rehlin, Rehlin Graphics, Ann Arbor, MI

This book is dedicated

To the thousands of innocent victims of Parkinson's who don't know where to go next. Their future, believe it or not, may be brighter than they think.

In addition, this book is dedicated to the many care-partners who provide invaluable help to us when we need it and ask for it. Most of the time, we couldn't make it without you.

Acknowledgments

How many times can you express your appreciation to the doctor and staff who have preserved your life and helped you to defeat the disease that was making it difficult to live?

A thousand times?

A thousand times thousand?

That's the way I feel about the team that took me through surgery and made it possible for me to enjoy a handicap-free lifestyle once again. Especially Dr. Fred Junn, who handled the surgery so deftly. Even his finishing touches were incredibly well done, and you can hardly tell I ever had surgery.

Dr. Richard Trosch, who has been a godsend since we moved closer to our grandbabies. Dr. Dragos Mihaila, who is a fellow working with Dr. Trosch, is a breath of fresh air. Since he is just starting his career, we wish him nothing but good things in the future. Head Nurse, Jeanne Draggoo, R.N.,is about as good as they come. She's competent, loyal, hard-working, and effective—and a little under-appreciated. Helping me throughout this difficult process were the wonderful nurses of Beaumont hospital, including Michael Cummins, Jane Carter, and Patricia Aldridge.

I'd also like to thank Actor Michael J. Fox for his tireless efforts to stamp out Parkinson's disease in our lifetime and for his magnificent fundraising efforts in our behalf. There are a lot of people shuffling around, wondering what to do with this disease, and wondering what the heck is happening with their jobs, their family lives, and their lives in general. They, like me, fall into the rut of bewildering hopelessness and confusion that snags all Parkinsonians at one time or another.

I'm not a doctor, a surgeon, a technician nor even an expert. I'm just the guy down the street, your typical guy, your next door neighbor, the fellow who was able to turn his Parkinson's condition upside down and begin looking to the future… optimistically for a change.

I can't say enough for my loyal care partner, Nancy. She has seen me at my worst, and now I hope she will see me at the other end of the spectrum. She has been in my corner all the while, from start to finish. (With a wink, she says that if I get to be a rich and famous author, she'll take the rich part). And my three sons, who stood by while I was at my worst points in the hospital.

After I returned home, number 1 son Scott gave me invaluable help in editing the script. Also, my good friend Mike Hogan in Peoria, Arizona, was a tremendous help in improving the copy. I owe you big time, Mike.

If you are a victim of Parkinson's, I have one objective: I hope this book, if nothing else, will bring you hope.

"Never Bet on a Horse
Who Has Parkinson's"

—Woody Allen, in
"Curse of the Jade Scorpion"

Preface

I didn't write this book for amusement.
I didn't write it for the money.
I didn't write it for fame.
And I didn't bet on a horse with Parkinson's. I wrote it, first, for other Parkinson's patients who might be in a muddle about the disease and the effects they could be experiencing for the first time. As I learned long after finding out that I had Parkinson's, no two patients react to treatment or medications the same way. Remember that: NO TWO PATIENTS REACT TO TREATMENT OR MEDICATIONS THE SAME WAY.

That's why the doctor is unable to sit and plot a long-term course of action with you. He just can't tell how the disease will affect your body. But there is one thing you can count on: *you're not going to like it. There's very little fun in Parkinson's.*

None of the symptoms are a walk through the park. And the whole package will overwhelm you for awhile, so don't get excited or depressed, because you're going to change the way you do things.

My wife and I have headed into this storm and are still splashing around, though we have achieved definite progress in recent weeks. To me, it's unbelievable that after all the excitement and all the fun I've had in my active life, I would wind up as an invalid. A **cripple**. It can't be. Actually on most days, I'm not. *There are no two days in which the body's reaction to the disease is exactly the same*. But there are important things to be learned when we compare our own situation to another's.

My second reason for writing it is to spread the word on some of the marvelous advances taking place in medical science. Doctors aren't the best marketers of their skills. Unless we shine some light on them, some of our finest talent and research expertise will go unnoticed in these important years ahead.

I can't praise the expert skills and in-depth knowledge of my doctors enough. They performed spectacularly well, and I owe my quality of life to them.

Third, I wrote it because I felt it would be interesting for readers to look through my eyes and feel through my skin the challenges and obstacles that inhabited my life every single day that are above and beyond the problems we all face as normal human beings.

Through the many Parkinson's seminars we have attended over the years, I've found that each workshop was effective if I could glean at least one good idea or piece of information that is immediately helpful to me. Therefore, I feel that if the Parkinson's victims reading this book get one good idea or suggestion that will improve their lives, then my objectives will be achieved. After all, it is the other people—those who have the disease and don' t seek treatment—who need all the support and just plain love that we can give to them.

Fourth, I wrote it for the thousands of care partners who share in the burden. The illness isn't something that's "owned" by the victim, but shared by the family and friends of the victim. I hope you, as care partner, will gain a better understanding of what's behind some of the patient's attitudes and actions.

I am pleased to bring my own experiences to your mind. If you have something to add, please write me at P.O. Box 636, Clarkston, Michigan 48347 or drop me a note online at <u>Kordene@ bignet.net</u>.

Table of Contents

Introduction

(DBS Minus Several Years)

Since the moment, almost ten years ago, when I became aware that I had Parkinson's Disease, it was obvious to me that the symptoms I dreaded most were, like a platoon of slow moving tarantulas, creeping insidiously up on me almost by the day. At the time when it was determined that I was a Parkinson's Disease patient, the only symptom I had was a stiff left arm and I was given just four pills per day to control the effects. At the time I went into Deep Brain Stimulation surgery, on the other hand, I was gobbling 21 pills per day just to keep pace with the disease, sacrificing my evenings without medication so I could keep a lid on the number of pills I would take each day. As a result of the drugs, I was up and down just about every day. If you think of a horizontal line as normal, my fluctuations were considerably above and below the line, depending upon how intense the medications were.

In the original diagnosis, the neurologist said that I fit the Parkinson's profile, which includes these symptoms:

(1) Tremors. Sometimes tremors may spread to your whole arm, which is what happened to me. I started a back and forth motion with my fingers, known as pill rolling. Also, I experienced (2) Slowed motion (bradykinesia) Eventually, I had other problems, but I never had difficulties with swallowing, digestion, or constipation.

(3) Rigid muscles and rigidity. A big problem that I experienced and continue to experience. Even my handwriting was affected.

(4) Blinking, smiling, and swinging your arms are all problematical when you have Parkinson's and I have experienced all of them. (5) Speech impairment. Many Parkinsonians have trouble speaking, but I,

fortunately, do not. I never had any problem with this symptom.

On some days, when I knew that I would be playing the piano, being productive, or socializing in the evening, I would take an extra Sinemet or Permax to grease up my joints and provide at least the facade of normal behavior.

But, as I mentioned earlier, with the heavy dosage of medication came pronounced highs and lows, periods when my system was over or under medicated and trouble was looming in River City.

Surgery, we were told, was out of the question. My neurologist said that it was reserved for the worst cases, and I was "too good" to be considered for an operation. When I heard that, I figured that I'd be going under the knife in five or ten years. In the meantime, I guess I would just deteriorate further. Then the doctors changed their minds, based on the conclusion that younger, less severe cases had a much greater chance for success through surgery, and that surgery would severely reduce or even eliminate the need for meds. It could also address stiffness, and shakiness that is characteristic of the Parkinson's condition. My fingers were so weak, it was impossible for me to open a small foil bag of peanuts on a plane; to button buttons and dress in the morning without help; or to get my shoes on without assistance.

Before surgery, there were times when I became utterly helpless, unable to make my arms and legs move or do anything I wanted them to do.

My balance, once sure and steady, was shaky and occasionally out of control. I sometimes walked as if I was sloshed with booze, a phenomenon that is doubly frustrating:

First, I occasionally look like the old actor, the late Foster Brooks, on a bad day. Foster was the consummate drunk, staggering around the stage of game shows he played on TV. Second, I didn't have the opportunity to drink the booze that would have created that degree of drunkenness. In other words, I didn't even feel good and I didn't drink anything to look like I was "feeling good".

I actually carry around a card that informs people that I'm a Parkinsonian so that someone won't think I'm drunk.

Suddenly, getting in and out of a car becomes problematical, though for years I took it for granted. When my joints have stiffened, every car seems like a Corvette to me. I have to fold my body in half before I get in, then aim my rump into the bucket seat. At the same time, I have to fold my head under the door frame and get it inside the car, with my hair all frazzled. My right leg often gets stuck under the steering wheel, so my next challenge is getting that leg to free up. Once that's done, I can pretty well jostle both of my feet onto the floor of the car. If the left leg isn't in properly, the door won't close when I slam it against my left leg. Then I lower the steering wheel until it bangs on my thighs and gives me a charley horse. This whole process used to be so easy!

In fact, everything used to be so easy. I wonder if I really sat down when I was normal and thanked the Lord for giving me over 50 years of a reasonably good life. During that time, I could do almost everything that a normal person could, and then it all ended. Thanks, Lord.

It has become so difficult to enter and exit our cars that we decided to sell both of our used low-slung models and purchase a new mini van, which is much easier to slide into and out of.

There's another activity I used to take for granted, going to the bathroom. Sometimes I have to forego a trip to the men's room because I know I can't zip my fly shut or button the top of my pants. And each trip to the toilet has become an adventure full of unanticipated horrors.

Furthermore, there have been awful side effects from some of the medications that pushed me farther and farther away from reality and established a kind of second personality that weakened my relationship with my wife, confused my fellow employees at the printing company where I was employed as a vice-president of marketing, and mystified other people upon whom I depended for support in my professional and personal worlds. The lifestyle that I anticipated, based on input from my original neurologist, and the lifestyle I led at this point were two different things, creating a very complicated life for myself and those around me. Whenever I tried to simplify it, I just dug myself a deeper hole, and now it was almost impossible to extricate myself from it.

It was like the tip of an iceberg that was revealing more and more of itself each day as it began to overwhelm my ability to function as a normal human being.

I made up my mind early in my battle with the disease that I was not going to give in to its challenges and threats. If I did, it would be all over and I would become a pathetic, miserable old man incapable of maintaining any semblance of normal social contact.

Since I was born a Taurus, I stubbornly honored my pledge that I was going to fight my condition with all of my being and to live life to the fullest against all the odds the disease could bring to the battlefield. And now I have a much better chance to win.

I like the comparisons of periods of history in terms of revolutionary breakthroughs in society. You know, the thought that we have experienced more inventions in the past 50 years than in all the years since Jesus Christ walked the earth? Well, the same kind of progress is being made in the field of medical science.

Before they talked with me about the DBS operation, I had already made up my mind that if the opportunity presented itself, I would run, not walk, to the nearest O.R. and get my name on the list. With or without cane.

I decided immediately that there would be no possibilities of losing my life in the surgical process. This team was just too sharp and experienced for that. My risk, then, was that the surgery wouldn't work. If that was the case, then I'd be even with where I was before the surgery. So what would we have lost?

Just time and $70,000 of the insurance company's money.

CHAPTER ONE

For Background

(DBS Minus Two Weeks)

I lived with Parkinson's for about ten years before I decided I had to take a major step if I was going to have any chance of regaining my abilities to handle life's most basic functions.

While I was considering Deep Brain Stimulation surgery, I ran across an article that summarized results of previous operations. It is so comprehensive in its coverage, I felt it was important to reproduce the entire article for your information:

BY KAWANZA L. GRIFFIN
Of the Journal-Sentinel Staff

Last Updated: Oct. 21,2001

About seven years ago, Jack Christensen began to notice a slight tremor in his body when he laughed. But then it got progressively worse.

His hands began to shake uncontrollably, making it hard for him to write, and soon he found himself becoming frustrated because he was unable to do something as simple as lift a spoon.

"I would try to put a straw through a hole and it would take me 45 minutes to do what it should have taken 30 seconds to do," Christenson said.

Christensen was diagnosed with Parkinson's disease and initially took medications to replace dopamine, the brain chemical whose deficiency leads to the condition. At first, that helped him to control his tremors enough to continue his daily activities.

The surgery was well worth it, says Christensen.

"Parkinson's disease itself doesn't hurt," he said. "It's just the constant motion that drives you up a wall."

DBS was first approved as an <u>experiment</u> by the Food and Drug Administration in July 1997 as a proven means of stimulating the thalamus, the region of the brain that processes and relays information before it goes to the muscles, to help control tremors in people with Essential Tremor or Parkinson's disease.

About 2 million Americans have Essential Tremor, a disorder that causes violent shaking. Another 1.5 million have Parkinson's, a neurological disorder characterized by progressive muscle rigidity, tremors and difficulty in moving. The decision to approve the device came after a study found that it reduced tremors by 58% in Essential Tremor and 67% in Parkinson's.

According to a report in the New England Journal of Medicine, thalamic stimulation works better than conventional thalamotomy in controlling severe tremors from Parkinson's and other diseases because it has fewer adverse effects and results in a greater improvement in function.

Thalamotomy is a decades old operation that destroys overactive, tremor-causing brain cells by burning or freezing a pea-sized spot in the brain. But it leaves many patients with speech problems, weakness or numbness. Actor Michael J. Fox had a thalamotomy for Parkinson's.

Despite the study, not everybody is sold on Deep Brain Stimulation. Paul A. Nausieda, medical director of the Regional Parkinson Center at Aurora Sinai Medical Center, said that although the procedure seems to be gaining popularity across the nation, many physicians are hesitant about it because its ability to improve quality of life remains to be determined.

"Just because the patient doesn' t die and doesn't have a tremor doesn't necessarily mean that they're better," he said.

Nauseida, one of the leading national experts on the disease, says he has seen patients who are frustrated after having the procedure because they still have symptoms of the disease besides tremors. He believes that for many patients, a combination of medications and "psychological discussion" is more beneficial.

Deep Brain Stimulation "is an aggressive procedure in a disease that's not fatal and one that has other treatment alternatives," he said.

"If used for tremors, it's not a bad treatment. But do you want to treat someone with a surgery that is so limited and so expensive?"

Ali R. Rezai, co-director of the Center for Functional and Restorative Neuroscience, and an associate professor in the department of neurosurgery at the Cleveland Clinic Foundation, is more enthusiastic about the procedure.

"This technology is safer than what's already out there... (and) the outcomes are pretty good."

Rezai, who is considered one of the leading national figures on the procedure, said that the system could even provide a treatment alternative for patients with tremor due to multiple sclerosis, epilepsy, chronic pain or some psychiatric disorders.

"We're just at the tip of the iceberg now,"
he said.

The stimulation device,known as the Active Tremor Control System, was developed by Medtronic Corp. of Minneapolis and consists of an electrode, an electronic device called the neurostimulator that provides the electric pulse and an extension wire to connect the two parts. When activated, the device sends a continuous flow of electrical impulses to the brain, blocking the brain signals that cause tremor.

The reason Deep Brain Stimulation seems to work has not yet been determined.

The procedure is now being offered at other state and local hospitals, including the University of Wisconsin hospital and clinics in Madison. "As it becomes more accepted by the medical community and the results keep coming, word will get out that it works and more doctors will offer it," said Brad Hiner, director of the movement disorder clinic at Marshfield. "However, it isn't a cure... it can help patients who are taking more and more medications but getting less and less benefit or experiencing more side effects."

Hiner, who treated Christenson, said that patients who have had the procedure tend to decrease their medications over time. But, he said, "it is uncertain how long the benefits of stimulation last, because patients have been followed for only about six years.

So far, Christenson is convinced.

"It causes an emotion that's really strong. I even shed a tear or two."

Christenson said he decided to undergo the procedure twice because he wanted to "live like a human again" and that being able to do

7

so has made the numerous 500 mile round trips from Crookston, MN., to Marshfield, WI worth every cent of his gas. "I feel very fortunate," he said.

Implanting the Device

To perform the procedure, surgeons first locate their target in the brain with Magnetic Resonance Imaging (MRI) or computed tomoraphy (CT) scans, then tightly attach an external head frame with a coordinate system to help them visualize the brain's internal structures. After numbing the skin, an incision of about an inch is made in the top of the head just behind the hairline and a nickel sized hole is drilled through the skull.

The surgeon then attaches micro electrodes on the thalamus, located in the deeper layers of the brain. While taking readings of brain activity, the surgeon monitors how well the patient can answer questions and follow directions. Extreme caution is taken because an incorrect placement could cause double *vision, tingling in the arms and legs, or a stroke.*

"You know you're in the right spot because the hand stops shaking," said P. Charles Garell, director of the functional neurosurgery program and an associate professor of neurological surgery at UW Medical School.

"The response is immediate. The tremor stops!"

In that article, you got a picture of Jack's dilemma, which is different from mine, which is different from my friends, which is different, etc.

I will tell you how I was affected by the dreaded disease and how I fought the battle to overcome the obstacles the disease was laying before us.

Spears and shields, please.

CHAPTER TWO

Cause And Effects

As a society, we have been chasing after the causes of Parkinson's Disease for decades, with little conclusive data to show for it. However, recent research indicates that genes play a more major role in Parkinson's than originally thought. That conclusion rules out environmental causes, which had been previously a significant part of the research equation.

That changes my thinking. I used to feel that I got the disease by eating unwashed fruit in my dad's grocery store. His supply of produce came right from the field (via Marchese brothers' trucks) to our store, and I had a habit of picking out an apple or orange and consuming it before my mom warned me to wash it.

So when she actually got to me, I would respond: "Oh Yeah," and repeat the same thing the next time Marchese showed up. I guess freshness was the main issue with me at that point.

I also thought that environment had something to do with it when I found out that four men had Parkinson's out of a work group of about 20 at my company. Perhaps asbestos, or something in the building, brought on the disease. But the research report splashes cold water on those "findings," and I have to go along with them. In that case, I hope that my grandchildren and great-grandchildren find that they can avoid the disease by just swallowing a pill or taking a shot. In my own family, no one really knows whether I had a Parkinson's-afflicted relative. In the past two or three generations, everyone seems to believe there was no single person who demonstrated Parkinson's symptoms—except me.

CHAPTER THREE

Attitude Is Everything

Recently, I saw a guy on a TV game show who seemed to laugh at everything. He started with a big smile, cracked a few jokes, and soon had everybody around him laughing and enjoying the moment. It was his attitude that affected both his disposition and the reaction of other people to him. If he showed up in the midst of a group gathering, everyone would crowd around him and try to feed off of his positive attitude.

From the first day I knew I had Parkinson's Disease, I have been determined to not let it beat me. To me, losing the battle is unacceptable, and *I will not let it destroy me.*

Once that was settled, I looked at my options for the future and decided that I could (1) Play on everyone's sympathy for me and whine about my burden ad infinitum, making everyone else miserable at the same time, or (2) Take a positive approach, living life to the fullest, and working to make others happy.

Like most of you, I chose the latter, and I feel I'm on track toward a successful cure within my lifetime. As for my lifestyle, I rarely sit around and do nothing. Instead, I'm always on the move, always looking for something interesting or someone interesting to talk about, think about, or write about. I really enjoy life and living, and I eagerly look forward to every new day.

Some Parkinson's patients get depressed about their condition, and I'd have to say that it is easy to see why. You might already be confined to a wheel chair or for some other reason, are at the mercy of the disease. How on earth did you let the disease get this far?

If you are working with a good neurologist, you should be getting some relief from the medications he doles out. Are you taking them?

I like to be a productive person despite the disease, but in time, your fitness for work and other fulfilling activity goes down rather dramatically. When I wrote my first book in 1996, I did it at night and on weekends while carrying a full load of work at the office. I have to be honest with you, however. I had someone in my corner all the time, and I always thought that the project would be completed on time and on budget. The weekly class sessions insured that I would keep the project on track. While I was taking the course, I often had to stand in the hallway and get control over my equilibrium before going into class. I didn't want the other students, nor the professor, to see me steadily losing it.

I guess that is really the most depressing thing about Parkinson's that bugged me a lot. I felt that each week put me further away from normality, and for awhile I didn't see any reversal. Now I see, and I feel, the reversal. That light at the end of the tunnel is not another train about to crash into me, I learned. It's the light of Dr. Junn and others like him that I haven't met yet, the light that's leading me out of the depression that sometimes consumes Parkinsonians.

I really don't care what other people think about me and I don't worry about things out of my control. Like Popeye the Sailor Man, "I yam what I yam" and what you sees is what you gets. I try to stay within my known capabilities and yet I push myself to excel, to be as productive as a person my age can be. I don't look over sixty, I don't feel over sixty and I don't think like an old person.

My dad was 46 when he died, and he was an old 46. Although he was a super gentleman, he never got out of his grocery store to find out what life had to offer, and he got into a terrible rut in a failing business. When I expressed an interest in carrying forward the business, he wouldn't hear of it. He insisted that I go to college and prepare for a job that paid a regular salary check and one that had a decent future.

He gave up on life in his forties, let himself get far out of shape, drank and smoked too much, and departed far too early. He never met his grandchildren, and they never had the benefit of his love. It was a terrible waste of the many talents and "smarts" with which he was blessed. And yet, while I may be critical of the way he lived his life, I can understand the trauma he must have experienced when his business succumbed to the supermarkets. After 30 years of independence in his own store, he suddenly found himself having to look for a job and work for someone else. Here's where the old dogs and new tricks come to the forefront.

He just plain gave up on life, something I never would think of doing.

Most people I meet for the first time would guess that I'm younger than I am, not pushing Social Security and Medicare. I ride my bike whenever I can and I walk a lot every day. I play the piano whenever someone wants to listen, and I stay up late and awaken early, trying to maximize the amount of time in every one of my days. I have very few wrinkles in my face or neck, and I'm still pretty damn strong, except when the Parkinson's takes over.

Sleep is a waste of time, in my view, and I'd do without it if I could, but I can't so I won't. I'm always busily chasing rainbows, trying to find that next idea that will capture my fancy and send me on another goose chase.

When they operate on my brain, I know they're going to succeed and my normal lifestyle will return. I feel positive because of their past track record and because I have confidence in their ability to change my life for the better.

There are a number of things that we would like to do in our remaining lifetime. We would like to travel through the Canadian Rockies, tour New England in the fall, Vienna anytime, and spend some time in the Pacific Northwest. But we were reluctant to take any of these trips because I couldn't predict how I would be feeling at any particular time.

I'd like to rent a motor home, but I couldn't even think of it when my Parkinson's condition was worsening.

When I have completely recovered from the surgery, one of my initial objectives will be to get a job. I haven't been able to work since 1997, and a part-time gig doing something productive would do a lot for me and my financial picture.

As the song says, "There's such a lotta livin' to do." You bet there is.

I have always thought that it was extremely important to exercise the mind. That's why I signed up for courses with Linda Peckham at Lansing Community College in "Writing for Publication." Being involved with my fellow students, doing homework, reading my own writing in class, all gave me a feeling that I was revisiting my youth. The brain is always thought of as a muscle of the body, just like all other muscles. So it needs to be exercised and kept active, and watching television all day and evening is not enriching to the brain, especially if you watch a steady diet of the idiotic talk shows on in the afternoon.

I have always loved music, and I found early in my musical career that I have some unique talents. I play the piano, but I don't play from sheet music. Although I can read music, I prefer to develop and arrange the songs I'm going to play from my own storehouse of musical knowledge.

In other words, I can pick out a tune, put some chords behind it, and develop an arrangement all "by ear." I've done this with about 300 songs, so I can play for over four hours without repeating a selection.

I started taking piano lessons at the age of 10 in a nuns' convent. My dad used me as a delivery boy for large grocery orders, and the nuns of St. John Kanty Parish in Milwaukee always welcomed with enthusiasm my arrival with groceries, at least once each week. They usually had warm cookies from the oven for me, and I basked in their attention while I unpacked their groceries from my coaster.

On one fateful day, the music teacher asked me if I would like to learn to play the piano in the living room of their convent. It was a heavy looking, foreboding, black, massive upright piano with deep keys, and was not particularly easy to play. I sat down at the keyboard and picked out a tune with one finger, and she smiled. A few minutes later, she produced a beginners' instruction book, and I was on my way.

I returned to the convent each day after school and practiced the elementary tunes and exercises included in the book. When that got to be old hat, I arranged to practice at the home of one of my special aunts and uncles, and finally I worked up enough courage to ask my dad to buy a piano so I could practice at home.

He gave me two reasons why I couldn't have my own piano: (1) He didn't have the money, and (2) We didn't have the space in our crowded home. So I tried an alternative approach and it worked. He rented a 12 bass accordion for me to vent my musical talents and, temporarily, my needs were satisfied. Now I could play whenever I wanted to, and I no longer had to walk to the nuns' home to practice.

He also signed me up for lessons at Randazzo Music on 13th street in Milwaukee. Johnny Randazzo was an accordion player of some limited renown on the south side, and dad entrusted my future in music to Johnny. He was a smooth talking, handsome guy who didn't mind everyone knowing that he liked to be the main attraction of every woman in town.

Unfortunately, Johnny was also a miserable music teacher. It turned out that he was an irresponsible lout who would spend most of my lesson time wandering around the store or talking with other customers while I struggled with some simple songs and exercises back in one of his mini studios. I found out early on that he was a poor instructor who didn't care whether I progressed or not. Magically, he always showed up when it was time to get paid for the lesson.

After a year or two of his hit and miss "lessons," I realized that I was going to level off pretty quickly in my playing ability if I spent any more time with Randazzo. So I encouraged my dad to buy a 120 bass accordion, which is the standard full-size model, and I expanded my practice time to learn songs that appealed to both my dad and to me.

Then Johnny announced that he was going to hold important music recital at the Polish American SPA(Society of Polish Americans) hall one evening in May. During my next lesson, he told me that he didn't have room for me in any of the bands scheduled to play for that recital, but that he would have me play solos between band presentations, while chairs and equipment were being moved around backstage. He assigned me about six boring songs that any simpleton could play and told me to practice hard for the recital.

I decided to outflank him, however. Without telling him, I had been working on some pop music and Slovenian dance tunes, and I decided that the recital would provide me with the opportunity to break out my own material.

So, with the rumble of chairs being pushed around on the stage behind me, I began to play a medley of favorite old standards that were known as popular dance tunes. Although the songs I was performing didn't even come close to the listing in their programs, the audience of parents and relatives reacted enthusiastically to my impromptu change of direction. And, because I had something to prove to Randazzo, I played my heart out that night during all of the intermissions. I didn't sit like the rest of the kids, I stood when I played, just like the pros.

After the first break, Randazzo came backstage and gushed over my surprise performance. "I didn't know you could play so well," he emoted. "How did you learn all those wonderful songs?" He knew all the time that he never gave me enough attention during lessons to have the slightest clue about my real ability and talents.

I stopped taking lessons shortly after that experience, because I found I was able to pick up popular songs, work them over my own way, and make them listenable in a fairly short time. When I was 16, my dad arranged for me to play in a local bar for $15 a night, so I continued to expand my repertoire of ethnic and pop songs, and soon I was making $20.00 nightly as part of a combo called the Kay-Tones.

The leader was a former school chum, Tony, who played the drums. To my left on the bandstand was Art, who played the alto saxophone. Both liked to consume a lot of beer, so our music got more raucous as the evening progressed. For the next 20 years or so, I concentrated on my business career and didn't play the accordion at all. Frankly, there wasn't much call for accordion music over those two decades. In my early forties, my wife and I decided to buy a baby grand piano for our living room, and I became interested in music once more. I spent countless hours at that keyboard over the next few years, transferring my knowledge of the board from the accordion to the piano, with detours to learn a decent left hand.

Whenever I went on the road for business meetings, I made a point of searching out the best piano at each hotel I stayed at, and would often play my entire repertoire on a gorgeous Steinway sequestered way back in the nooks and crannies of the hotel's staging facility.

Soon, after many hours of practice, I became a good enough piano player, self taught, that I could play in public.

So I performed whenever there was a handful of people to listen to me and provide encouragement. Each time I played, I got a little bit better until I began to amaze even myself with some of my playing. As my confidence grew, so did my taste in pianos. Now I'm playing in nicer environments and I am receiving positive reviews. I find that playing the piano is both mental and physical therapy. But I have to be continually vigilant about my medication schedule. Unmedicated, I can't play with the left hand at all, and my right hand gets very weak as well. Medicated, I can play as well as I have ever played.

Now, with my new "system" working, I can always play reasonably well, and I shouldn't have the low spots when I can't play at all. After the operation and" fine tuning," I have noticed that my fingers feel a lot more flexible and I can play more smoothly and pleasingly.

Earlier this year, I auditioned to play the piano at Nordstrom's department store near my home. Nordstrom's serenades its customers with piano music every minute of the day. They have nine pianists on their payroll, and a beautiful grand piano on the second level, next to the escalator. They don't pay much, but it's good exposure. I played there about five weeks, but the three-hour schedule was a little more than my body could handle. I found my fingers stiffening up toward the third hour, and I had to soak them in warm water during the two breaks. I left that job and will return when I can handle the physical side of playing the piano.

CHAPTER FOUR

What Are We Dealing With?

As you probably know, Parkinson's is a chronic, progressive degenerative disorder of the central nervous system that is diagnosed in 50,000 Americans each year, and more than a million people in the U.S. battle the disease every day. They have trouble getting out of bed, dressing, eating, and functioning as normal people. Most of them shuffle when they walk, speak slowly and quietly, shake a lot, and walk very gingerly. The fact that I was willing to be included on the 2001 schedule for surgery made the prospect for me very favorable with both Drs. Trosch and Junn.

Parkinson's results from the loss of cells in a section of the brain. In normal people, those cells produce dopamine, a chemical messenger responsible for transmitting signals within the brain. Loss of dopamine causes critical nerve cells within the brain to function out of control, leaving the victims unable to manage movement.

Symptoms include trembling, stiffness, rigidity (freeze ups), balance, weakness, and slowness. Occasionally, I have experienced a tremor that shook my whole body violently. But in about ten seconds, it was all over and I could have gone back to normal. When that happens, I lose my drink or ice cream dish and wind up cleaning up some kind of mess on the floor or on myself.

Although Parkinson's is not curable (YET), the disease is both progressive and treatable with appropriate drugs that substitute for the missing chemicals in the brain. Almost everyone you talk to remembers, in the past, their Aunt Trudy or Uncle Herbert suffering uncontrollably from the disease in their later years and couldn't make life livable with medications—because there were no such medications. They would shiver, and quiver, and shake, and everyone else in the family would stand around and feel sorry for the poor old folks, but there was nothing they could do for them, so they would put them away in a nursing home. From then on, they would shake and bake on their own.

When I reach a low in my medications, I feel like a puppet whose strings are loose. My limbs dangle and move out of sync, my head bobs, and my feet don't want to move at all. It's quite a pathetic thing to witness, but an even more pitiable condition to experience.

Two of the symptoms that cause problems are the stoic face and the swallowing mechanism in your throat. The flat, emotionless face is called the "Parkinson's Mask". When you are in a group of Parkinsonians, it appears that you're surrounded by a bunch of blank-faced folk who stare straight ahead and rarely smile. When I came in to be calibrated shortly after my surgery, the nurse remarked that my face showed emotion and animation, neither of which had been there before.

I like to smile and be positive, so I was glad that the mask was no longer part of my makeup.

The swallowing problem never existed with me. I have heard of Parkinsonians having difficulty chewing and swallowing, so I guess it is a problem for some. That's why they have me participating in a study involving the x-ray of my throat while I chew and swallow crackers dipped in barium.

Before I was diagnosed with Parkinson's Disease, I was reasonably active and generally kept myself in good physical condition. I played tennis every week, got in a couple dozen rounds of golf each year, and walked a mile or so every couple of days. I never have smoked, and my drinking has been very moderate.

Shortly after my diagnosis meeting in 1992, my wife sent me on a special trip to Lakeland, Florida, where I participated in a week-long fantasy camp with retired members of the Detroit Tigers and about 60 guys from the ages of 25 to 70. We took calisthenics, ran, and worked out daily with the whole group and individually, trying our best to get in reasonable shape for the games that were scheduled for late in the week. It was like being a kid again, that unforgettable era in my life when I took to the field and enjoyed the sport, the sun, the teammates, and the absence of cares.

In 1997, I went to a second Detroit Tiger fantasy camp. This time, I was thrilled to pitch two innings on the mound of beloved Tiger Stadium, where baseball was played by Ty Cobb and thousands of other luminaries before the park was abandoned in 1999. The fact that the batters were as far out of shape as I was faded from my mind as I reached back into my athletic past to get the ball over the plate and make it difficult to hit.

It was a great thrill to find myself throwing that same 60'6" that was thrown by Denny McLain, Mickey Lolich, Hal Newhouser, Jim Bunning, Dizzy Trout, and hundreds of well-known and hated opposing pitchers like Whitey Ford, Bob Gibson, and Herb Score.

I pitched two innings and gave up about four meaningless runs. The first guy up swung on the third pitch and hit the ball off the left field wall, which traditionally would have meant a triple to the batter.

I went to cover third base and found that he had stopped at first to catch his breath, and he had no visions of second base, much less third base, in mind.

To me, the highlight of the Fantasy camp was the appearance of my grandson Nicky, who had a chance to see his grandpa acting like a baseball player and doing it in a place that had a magnificent history. He'll have a lot to tell his grandkids.

Or, the highlight may have been Jon Warden, former relief pitcher with the Tigers, who said on the first day: "We have a philosophy about the way we do our work around here. We start off slow, then taper off."

I liked the tapering off part. Since my physical condition has deteriorated due to the impact of Parkinson's, I have drastically reduced my physical activities. I tried playing softball a year ago, but found that I would easily lose my balance and several times wound up with my chin in the turf, cleat marks down my back and my clothes full of sod stains. I decided then and there that I shouldn't try to be the second coming of Mickey Mantle as planned, and considered alternative ways to exercise for health.

However, this strategy became problematical, too, because of the difficulties I had with dressing and undressing. It took me more than a half hour to change clothes, and there were no guarantees that I would be able to fasten the button at the top of my fly.

Anticipating a disastrous episode with a button has caused me to rethink my travel plans. It is extremely difficult for me to handle buttons, especially if the waistband of my pants is tight. Therefore, I can't go out by myself unless I am absolutely certain I can handle my bathroom routine. In a couple of embarrassing episodes, I had to ask a men's room attendant to help button the top button, explaining the fact that I have a handicap and was in dire straits.

One result of this awkward dilemma is that I simply avoid going to the bathroom. I am fortunate to have strong kidneys, and have never required trips to the bathroom at night. And my medications cause my system to be backed up, so I can live without a pit stop all day.

There have been days when I was so weak during a low period that I couldn't lift up my pants after a bathroom visit. Reluctantly, I must call upon my wife to perform a task she used to handle with our sons when they wee little boys. Occasionally, my predicaments are so ridiculous, we both break down laughing. But not for long.

Balance is a good example of my challenges. When I am covered by medication, I can ride a bike and walk quite normally. But as the meds dip down in effectiveness, I walk like I am on a mattress and I have real problems standing in place for any extended period of time. I have to be constantly on the move, or I wobble and shuffle like the silhouette figures in a shooting gallery.

Still another symptom of Parkinson's is a nervous leg or foot. In my case, it's the left foot that just keeps moving and shaking, and I simply cannot put on the brakes and make it stop. So you'll have to put up with it, no matter how distracting it is.

In the planning of our surgery, our designated coordinator from the neurologist's office put us through a pleasant orientation about the procedure and, through her descriptions, we were able to get a much better perspective on the new approach.

After reviewing my file, she said she thought that I would be a good candidate who would probably benefit most from this type of surgery, since I was young and in decent health.

She had high praise for the surgeon who would handle the operation. "You'll like him, I'm sure," she said. "He's one of the nicest, most caring people I have ever met. The two of you will work well together."

As I reviewed the experiences of other patients, I was reminded that tremors and shaking were not the problem. I had trouble typing, playing the piano, and getting up from a soft chair. Would DBS solve that problem?

She went on to say that patients who were candidates for the Deep Stimulation Implant surgery were organized into groups of 20, and she felt that there was at least one opening in the next group. *I wanted that opening!*

She gave us some examples of patients who had undergone the surgery and outlined the improvements that were experienced by each one. One patient she cited was requiring 15 Sinemets each day before the operation and dropped down to only five daily after surgery. Since I was only at the five level now, there appeared to be a good chance that I could eliminate the medications entirely through the surgical process.

She said the next step was to line up an appointment with the surgeon as soon as our schedules permitted. We discussed September dates and she said she would call me as soon as an opening in his schedule would present itself.

CHAPTER FIVE

Lucky In Life

Throughout my adult life, I have considered myself to be very fortunate. The word "fortunate" is derived from "fortune" or wealth, and as far as life's interesting experiences stack up, I've had a wealthy existence. You may think that I am nuts, having fought with Parkinson's for so long, but hear me out. I have a great family, a loving spouse who is one of the finest people anyone could know, a nice home, and a series of fascinating personal and professional experiences that elude most people through their life spans.

I've earned good incomes throughout my working days, salted a chunk of it away, and we enjoy a good standard of living. We were also fortunate to have a steady stream of fringe travel benefits flowing our way. I had responsibilities for the development of a Europe wide advertising campaign for five years in the seventies, and I was required to be in Europe three times each year for about three weeks each time. I directed the work of ten small advertising agencies in the conversion of a distributor directed program to a company program. During that period, I learned a great deal about the European continent and met a bunch of people who were helpful to our process of learning. Again, we were the beneficiaries of good luck when my wife was invited to join in some of the international travel.

Then, when I changed jobs, my travel was more specifically concentrated on trips to New York city, where we entertained important clients at Tavern on the Green or Christ Cella, very exclusive restaurants, and took in Broadway plays, the Metropolitan Opera, or the ballet.

Of course, my spouse accompanied me at the company's expense.

A couple of job changes later, I became responsible for liaison between my company and thirty or so partners all over the globe, so our international travel began anew. Our life was enriched by all of the travel experiences and we made new friends wherever we went.

The trips were not all exactly holiday excursions. We traveled with my chairman of the board and his wife, and there was a certain amount of brown nosing and hand holding involved. My boss had a habit of making crude, insulting remarks to our hosts, so I spent a lot of time smoothing over the turf after he had infuriated the Europeans, South Africans, New Zealanders, or Aussies.

Also, it was my responsibility to present our marketing programs and allow our partners to pass judgment on them versus each of their own efforts. The fact that I won four out of five competitions and brought home the gold first place trophy each time solidified my standing in the international community.

During all of this travel, my Parkinson's condition was a minor factor. I remember how

I broke the news to my boss that I was suffering from the illness. We were having breakfast at the Marriott hotel in London, England, prior to one of our partner meetings to be held in Cambridge.

He had just finished his bowl of oatmeal when I asked him if he had any friends or acquaintances, or family members, who had Parkinson's Disease. When he answered in the negative, I responded: "Well, now you have." He was extremely sympathetic and told me, for the first of many times, that he would see to it that my job was tailored to take advantage of my creative talents, and that if any changes in my responsibility were needed to accommodate any aspects of the Parkinson's condition, he would make those changes and protect our position within the company.

"TELL US WHAT YOU NEED, AND WE'LL PROVIDE IT," HE SAID.

Five years later, he fired me. So much for promise keeping.

Well, that was one way to get rid of the stress that came with the job. The question that my wife and I had to face, with all of the health uncertainties, our aging, and our income needs was "What's Next?"

Through all of my career, my health had been generally good. The only time I missed work for any length of time was in the late seventies, when I had to have some work done on my prostate gland, which grounded me for six weeks. A few years later, I was in and out of the hospital within a week after the repair of a hernia.

In the last two years of my final corporate job, however, the Parkinson's condition became more of a factor in my day to day work. First of all, I had to stop what I was doing two or three times each day to take my meds on a timely schedule. Outwardly, I began to show signs of the disease, particularly when I walked through the halls of our office and manufacturing facilities.

I had to have my medications early, before noon, so I generally went to lunch at about 11:15 each day. That arrangement made it possible for me to be up on meds for the afternoon meetings. Also, my left arm became less and less mobile, and I began to walk stiffly. Other than that, there were few indications that I had a debilitating disease, because I was still in the early stages of Parkinson's and I disguised a lot of my stiffness and dyskenesia. But the question still remained. What Next?

At the time I left the company, I had already published my first book, which was written at night, on weekends and during trips and delays in airports. It was called "Holding Pattern: Airport Waiting Made Easy," and we used it to launch a new career: book publishing.

Since I worked for a printer who wanted desperately to cultivate an image as a creative resource for the horticulture industry, they loved to introduce me as their "resident author," have me sign books, and promote my book among customers to the extent that they, the company, would reimburse me for any books I gave away in the normal business week.

But after 35 years of career success and growth, I had had enough of the corporate world and now I would work at home, avoiding traffic, back stabbers, frauds, B.S.ers, and all other undesirable species that inhabit the corporate jungles these days. I was delighted.

A whole new world had opened up for me and for my family. Luck? You could say so, but I'd prefer to consider it good fortune.

The first book had a lot of P.R. value, and I managed to get over 100 interviews on radio talk shows all over the U.S. as well as a 20 minute feature on CNN Airport and a splash in the New York *Times*.

The CNN interview came about in an unusual way. About six months after the book HOLDING PATTERN: AIRPORT WAITING MADE EASY was released, I noticed on a distribution report that two copies were being shipped to Turner Broadcasting Co. in Atlanta. I decided to send a letter along, and in the letter I let Turner know that I was available to assist if they needed any help. A few weeks later, I received a return letter from the president of CNN Airport Network, the vehicle by which programming from CNN is piped to the TV sets in the waiting areas of airports all over the world—1100 gates, in fact. That was a perfect audience for my book.

Anyway, the letter was critical of the fact that CNN Airport was not mentioned in the book as an activity that can help you pass the time when your plane is late or your flight is canceled. When I received the correspondence, I called the network in Atlanta and told them that my second book, WHY YOU SHOULD TAKE YOUR TRAVEL AGENT TO LUNCH, would be out shortly, and that I would be happy to include some copy about the network. In a couple of weeks, I received a PR kit, from which I could develop the copy.

When a proof of the story became available, I sent it to the president of CNN Airport. Several days later, I received a phone call asking me to be in Atlanta on a specific date for an interview. So I hustled down with a stack of books under my arm and wound up with a 20 minute exposure to the passengers waiting at 1100 gates at various airports throughout the world, at a cost of about $400 for travel and expenses.

Throughout my stay at CNN, they treated me like a celebrity. I got to tour the studio, meet several notable anchors, and roam around as if I were Ted Turner Jr. It was an exceptional experience and one I will remember for a long time.

CHAPTER SIX

The Feeling Is Weird

Most people don't have any idea of the tension and pressure a handicapped person goes through when they want to do something and can't make their body parts work the way they should. Most handicapped people are not full of jokes and fun, and maybe this is why.

About seven years after my diagnosis, I began to have freeze-up moments when I just couldn't move. When I described the feeling to my doctor, I used the terms "paralytic" and "catatonic" because I felt simply helpless and unable to get my body to cooperate with my mind.

Sometimes, the feeling is like that of a drunkard who can't make his feet walk a straight line to save his skin (and driver's license). But more often it is the lack of a response from the legs or arms that a Parkinsonian must deal with.

You know damn well what you want to do, but you just can't do it. Getting out of a car, for example. You know the door is open and you need to move your feet to the pavement below, but your legs refuse to honor the commands of your mind. You try to build some momentum by rolling your upper body forward, but your feet still won't respond. Although the hands aren't much more co-operative, you get one hand down on your right leg and push it strongly enough so that it (your leg) plops out onto the driveway. Then, leaning on your right foot, and grasping the top of the door frame, you conjure up enough strength to pull yourself through the door opening and into a standing position, but a very shaky one at that. The same struggle takes place when you inadvertently sit in a very soft chair or couch. Your joints are rigid and you feel wobbly, but you shift your feet around and balance yourself.

I don't like to need help and I don't like to be watched while I'm going through these maneuvers because I imagine that I must look like Frankenstein playing out these contortions. I can understand the difficulty that actors and celebrities have with the disease, because it is so difficult to hide or disguise. It must appear that I'm acting out a role in a slow motion movie. But this is no movie. This is life.

After a few experiences like this, I found myself getting angry—at myself. But by becoming angry, I was able to achieve the task much faster than if I just grit my teeth and accepted the situation. This technique works particularly well when removing pants, I learned. A burst of strength while in a fit of temper turns out to be just what I need to extricate my foot from the pant leg.

It's not a good idea to have other people, especially children, around when you act out of anger. Some of the blue language I use during those moments would remove three layers of wallpaper and make a youngster think there was a maniac loose in the house.

Every person has their own shortcuts to handle life's basic functions. Some Parkinsonians who experience the freeze-up condition use a special cane to get themselves in motion and back in action. The cane has a white extension about 6" long at the bottom and the patient uses it as a kind of starting line. Once you put your foot over the starting line, it's supposed to give you the inertia to get moving and stay moving.

Another point of frustration is moving around at night. I never thought that I would have problems getting into bed at night, but it's one of the challenges I face daily... or should I say nightly. I have found that if I just lie down, my body is diagonal on the bed, or my head is up against the headboard, or some such thing. At that hour of the day, my legs have no strength at all, so I can't maneuver around very easily. So we remove the covers, and I sit on the edge of the bed and roll my body into place, spending the next ten minutes twisting and turning so that I'm positioned just right, 'cause that's where I'm going to stay. It's relatively impossible for me to change positions at night, so I can't have an arm under my head or my leg twisted in some uncomfortable way, for that's the way it's going to be the rest of the night. Then my wife slides the covers over me and I'm all set for the next five hours or so.

As a result of my limitations, I find myself consciously planning my next moves so I can be sure that I can handle them, especially when there are other people around. When Michael J. Fox announced his retirement from his tv program, he said that it was too difficult for him to act and remember all of the individual steps he had to accomplish in a scene. A Parkinsonian begins to map out his or her next moves, making sure that there are no barriers too great to overcome in their paths.

Crowds become a real challenge, because most people in a crowded room or store apparently have no clue as to where they are going and don't realize that I can't stop and start and weave left and right as crisply as they can. I often feel like a broken field running back in a football game, picking my way smartly down the field, trying to avoid tacklers (make that "obstacles") at every turn.

It's somewhat of an "out-of-body" experience, for you know you want to do, but can't make your body do it. That's when my blood begins to boil and I get violently angry because I'm so fricken frustrated.

In the consideration of surgery, there are several approaches you can take. The first thing you need to recognize is that there is no cure—just specific procedures that will attack specific symptoms. For those Parkinson patients who fail to respond to medication, there is a treatment called Pallidotomy, which consists of drilling a tiny hole in the skull and using an electric probe to destroy part of the global pallidus, which is overactive in Parkinson patients. Patients with disabling tremors in the hand or arm may consider thalodotomy, a procedure that destroys cells in the thalamus. It has no effect on the other symptoms of Parkinson's. Sometimes the surgeon will operate on one side at a time, but in my case they decided to do both at the same time.

Fetal tissue transplants have also been tried with limited success. This approach, like stem cells, is fraught with problems, from the ethical to the practical. It will be a long time before this kind of surgery sees the light of day.

Don't mistake other neurological conditions for Parkinson's. Some of them, like Essential Tremor, present similar characteristics, but the treatments vary widely. That's why it is a good idea to consult a qualified neurologist early in the game. He or she can give you an accurate diagnosis and prescribe some helpful drugs. But remember, that prescription is likely to be just for starters.

CHAPTER SEVEN

The Family Matters

We've learned many hard lessons in the past decade, and one of them is that we have to keep our family involved in dealing with the disease. They need to know that dad is no longer the guy they knew as children, and that no amount of hoping will bring back that funny, free-wheeling, active, productive guy who was always available to help them, no matter what challenge they faced.

Ignorance is a real enemy here, because if they don't know what the prognosis is, and what their expectations should be, they will be surprised and probably shocked when they find out what's really happening inside the Parkinsonian's mind and body.

I've been fortunate that my three sons, and the spouses of two of them, have a general idea of what we're facing and what we're doing to keep up the battle against our mutual enemy. I think they have all relied on us to tell them the facts, but I wouldn't be surprised if several of them have done some informal research on their own.

One difficulty I have is letting them see me in less than good condition. When I'm low on medication, my speech sometimes becomes slurred and my feet either shuffle like the little old man crossing the street, or stagger like I've had too much Molson's. When we're together for family outings, I sometimes get drowsy and my eyelids become heavy. I think my kids know that the sleepy look on my face has nothing to do with our conversation, or the last joke they told, but the heavy load of drugs I've taken every four hours.

Drowsiness is something I feel every time I stop what I'm doing and try to sit quietly and read or watch television.

When my wife drives, I often catch up my sleep from my perch in the passenger seat. My head rolls around loosely, like a bobble-head doll, and the seat belt keeps me from mortally wounding myself.

Stiffness in walking is another result of PD. Sometimes it takes me about 25 yards of shuffling before I am loose and able to walk relatively normally. I also drool, sometimes when I am talking with another person and the spit has to be wiped (thank God for my beard). In the meantime, I feel like Tim Conway, who's made a fortune imitating elderly people.

I feel embarrassed by those symptoms, but I can't do anything about them, so I have to let everything hang out, so to speak. Fortunately, the times I am able to act normally far outnumber the times I demonstrate my worst case condition.

On our trips to northern Michigan, I have occasionally become drowsy because of all the pills I guzzle down. If I'm driving alone, I turn up the local rock station and blast my ears for ten minutes every hour, to keep my alertness. If my wife is accompanying me, we trade off driving time and keep talking to each other so that we don't fall into a boredom ditch.

Eventually, I suppose I'll have to give up driving, but I'm being extra careful at this point to ensure that I don't experience any accidents. My concern is and will be that no one else is ever hurt because I decided to drive when I shouldn't have.

However, my ability to concentrate has become so acute, I'm actually a better driver at times now than before, because I don't let distractions take my eye off the road. I'm also very comfortable driving at night, when the darkness hides a lot of distracting signs and attractions. My greatest enemy is drowsiness caused by my medications. When we're on a trip and I'm driving, we carry on long conversations, play the radio louder, sing, and munch some crunchy snack.

I hope I'm not caught up in some false illusion, but I believe that my driving is not dangerous to anyone's health. My point total with the Secretary of State is very low right now and I intend to keep it there.

Life can be miserable for the Parkinsonian when he or she doesn't have all the medication they should have. On the opposite end of the spectrum is the condition I find myself in when I have built up the medication in my system and I feel "high." It's at this time that I feel "normal" and, as a result, somewhat euphoric.

Able to leap tall buildings in a single bound? That's me when I have a full dose of medication plus some buildup from earlier in the day. I can paint the ceiling without using a ladder, or dig up the entire backyard with a shovel, or climb Mt. McKinley simply because it's there. You name it, I can do it and usually do.

It's wonderful to have this feeling, but I can't sustain it for more than a few hours at a time. On the other hand, my wife feels I become reckless and somewhat obnoxious when I'm running high, so she can't wait until I come back down and become the kinder, gentler husband she thought she had married.

When I'm running high on meds, my kids have a problem keeping up with me. I'm here, there, and everywhere, and my personality becomes far more aggressive and extroverted than usual. I talk to anybody, about almost anything.

My attention span becomes shorter, and I tend to jump from one subject to another. Since I play the piano, I can roam over the keyboard with ease, playing like I did when I was 20 years old. Undermedicated, on the other hand, I lose my left hand entirely and my right hand becomes slower and less controllable. I sound like an 8 year old playing some ditty for the first time.

Since I started my pill popping regimen ten years ago, I have gained a much higher respect for the wonderful things that scientists have brought us in the pharmaceutical area. Without the drugs I'm taking, I would be nothing but a blob who wouldn't be able to take care of himself nor be productive in any way.

But the problems caused by some of the medications are legend in the neurological community. People of great wealth and power, people with jobs at the top of their companies, have destroyed their families and frittered away their savings with their compulsive behavior. Like many Parkinsonians, I had suicidal thoughts, though brief, for my life seemed headed for a dead end… a spiraling series of setbacks that led to nothing positive. I can agree with the Parkinson's patient who considers taking his or her own life, but I can't condone it. The hurt they leave behind with their care partners and others in their lives just doesn't justify the act, in my view.

One potential side effect of the drugs is a stimulated libido or, in other words, a significantly increased sex drive. Guys who up to that point who are psychologically normal suddenly find themselves chasing skirts like a teenager after a couple of beers. If it isn't some girl on the street corner, the victim is arranging for call girls.

Dr. Trosch told me that there were dozens of stories about the damaging exploits of Parkinson patients as a result of the compulsive side-effects of the medication. He said that a number of his patients went off the deep end at the casino, and others reported getting involved in prostitution, voyeurism, and a variety of nasty activities well out of the normal realm of the victims' social circles.

*   *   *

The last week before the operation was full of testing and observing, and the subject was me. I felt a little bit uncomfortable being in the spotlight, but I also enjoyed the special treatment I was getting from everybody. I get the feeling that she still hasn't figured out her value in the overall equation, but my wife hasn't stopped to ask questions. She just does what has to be done, and that's an immense help to me in dealing with the Parkinson's condition.

First of all, she is a source of strength to me emotionally. She keeps me on a positive, optimistic track, even when I break down in tears at the piano because I can't play as well as I used to. She's always renewing my faith, hope, and confidence that things will get better, not worse, and that we'll be able to live out our retirement years in comfort and with a degree of happiness.

When I first learned that I was a Parkinson's victim, I was alone—one on one—in the doctor's office. My reaction was relatively mild, for several reasons. One, I didn't know much about PD, and the tightly scheduled neurologist didn't paint much of a picture of what I could expect. His primary effort was to acclimate me to the application of medications starting the following day. Physically, she's doing more than ever before to help me. I often can't get out of my chair without help, and she is always there to give me a tug. Now, she has arthritis and a very bad knee condition, and sometimes she undergoes pain when she moves in to help me. But I never hear any whining or complaining—just expressions of willingness to help. When I'm getting dressed in the morning, she's there to help me pull my tee shirts over my head and shoulders. And when I'm showing signs of drowsiness while we're driving, she willingly takes over the wheel and makes it possible for me to catch a couple of z's in the passenger seat.

She's probably wondered why she finds herself in the position of a Care-Giver, and frankly I don't have a clue. But she's perfect for the role, because she has always been a warm, loving person who went out of her way to care for and support the people nearest her. I want her burden in future years to be as minimal as possible, so I'll do whatever it takes to regain normality in my neurological controls. She deserves to enjoy life to the fullest, and I will express my appreciation to her in all the ways her role can be recognized and rewarded. She knows that I'll return the favor if she ever needs my help.

Now that I am moving back to normality, it may be time for her to have her knee replaced, so she can avoid the terrible pain her mother underwent as an elderly lady. I am strongly in favor of her need to get the operations going. We've got a lot of boogie-ing to do before we hang up our spikes, baby.

First up in the testing sequence was the doctor from Romania., Dr. Dragos Mihaila, M.D. He put me through a battery of tests and scored his ratings from visual observation. Like several doctors before him, the researcher zeroed in on the lack of muscle between the thumb and forefinger of the left hand, a condition I've had for over 30 years.

I pointed out to him that I had a hairline fracture in my left elbow in the '70's from a tennis game warm up accident, and it may have affected the muscle in question. He looked it over again, shook his head, and went on with the tests. This first series was to be done with my system low in medication. I hadn't had any pills since 6 p.m the previous day.

He had me perform the usual finger, hand, and arm exercises, noting for the benefit of his assistant any rigidity or unusual movement of my arms and legs, particularly in the joints. He found quite a bit.

CHAPTER EIGHT

The Vagaries of the Mind

The longer we follow the Parkinson's path of life, the more we realize that we have to admit our limitations and make the necessary adjustments to live comfortably. For example, when I was working full time, I used to like to have a cocktail before dinner each night. It was a good time to relax and talk about the day's events, go through the mail, and so on.

Now, one week before surgery, cocktails and other alcoholic drinks are out because of the medication schedule and the dangers of mixing meds with liquor. So we drink iced tea and talk, which is much less expensive than slugging down a couple of martinis.

I have not been able to work for the past four years. When I was working, it was difficult for me to meet schedule deadlines and keep pace with my responsibilities because of the ups and downs of my condition.

I decided to write books and established an office in the lower level of my home, so I didn't have to face rush hour traffic each day. In recent years, I have noted a lack of productivity in the early morning hours due to my Parkinson's condition. I usually rise early, about 6 a.m., eat breakfast, and begin working around 8. But sometimes, my slowness and stiffness will keep me from doing anything worthwhile until later in the morning.

That problem is really a frustrating one. Here I am, up early, and I can't type worth a damn. When my medicines take over, I could out type probably 80% of the administrative assistants (secretaries) around.

Our business has been reasonably good, considering that we started from scratch and are in a very competitive marketplace. We write and produce our own books, advertise them, sell them, send them, collect the money, even vacuum the floor.

The Parkinson's condition slows me down to the point that there are some days when I cannot work at all. I get thoroughly disgusted and demoralized when that happens.

One overriding concern I have carried in my back pocket over the past ten years is the possibility of dementia resulting from the disease or the drugs I've been taking. I still harbor the thought that the deterioration of parts of the nervous system could result in reduced brain power.

A number of things have changed since I was diagnosed. First, in contrast to my ability during my working years, I'm unable to juggle many topics at one time. It used to be easy for me to entertain three or four trains of thought at one time and produce satisfactory conclusions in each of them.

Now I become confused when confronted with two or more subjects at a time.

For example, when I'm ready to leave the house and head for the post office, my mind has reviewed all of the key points of my trip and decided what I need to take along to complete the objectives of the trip. I may need the keys to our p.o. box. Check. I'll probably need $5.00 or more for postage. Check. Car keys? Check.

Now my wife asks me what we should have for dinner. In a second, I lose my concentration on the post office trip and now I'm focused on dinner meal selections. I am frustrated that I didn't conclude my trip checklist. At the same time, I am now devoting attention to the new topic. Nothing further on the other subject occurs to me until I have resolved the dinner suggestion request. In the past, I would have handled both topics with ease. While coming up with dinner ideas, I would have concluded the trip list and been on my way.

Sometimes I concentrate so intensely that I block everything else out of my mind and I'm shocked when someone else walks into the room, or when the phone rings. It's difficult for me to change gears and segue from one topic to another without a clean break, much like a manual transmission shift versus a smooth transition from gear to gear as in a car with automatic transmission.

I'm not sure my writing ability has been impacted, although it takes me about five times as much time to write something than it took ten years ago. Readers of my first book can measure any changes in style, clarity, or word selection and usage versus the quality of this piece.

Memory is not as good as it was, especially in remembering names. If I don't pay special attention to the person introducing me, I quickly lose track of the names of new people I have met.

Also, I tend to leave things behind absent-mindedly. Of course, my neurologist has a name for the problems I've experienced in this area: AGING. Thanks, doc.

Seriously, I guess I should have expected his response, considering that I am now into the Medicare stage.

In the musical area, I have maintained the ability to recall over 300 songs and play them on the piano without sheet music. That's about four hours of music, and the slightest stimuli can get me going on my almost endless song list.

I took a swallowing test today at Beaumont hospital. This is one of three in the series, and it's quite simple. All I have to do is swallow graham crackers soaked in barium, which is a white liquid that tastes like melted chalk.

The researcher started our session by squirting herself in the eye with barium. Ouch!

After chewing up and swallowing about ten of these crackers, I was sent on my way with $50.00 in hand, compensation for my trouble.

I'll be back in three months and one year after the surgery.

CHAPTER NINE

Decision is a No-Brainer

(DBS MINUS ONE MONTH)

My consultation with the doctor today was extremely informative and encouraging. Shortly after we arrived, his nurse interviewed me in depth to get a complete understanding of my condition at that time. She said she would be accompanying Dr. Junn and me into the operating room and would have the responsibility of keeping me alert and observing me during the surgery. She would later be the person who would program the device so that it would send the right signals to my brain. She, too, thought that I would be good candidate for surgery, based on her past experience with Parkinson's disease.

She observed that I was experiencing dyskenesia this morning; my head was moving quite a bit and the movement was out of my control. Earlier, I had taken my four medications at 6:30 a.m. and 10 a.m., and it was just about noon now. I had reached my peak and dyskenesia took over. Also, my speech began to slur but I couldn't do anything about it. My condition at that point looked a lot like Michael J. Fox's but, of course, he was a ton of years younger than me.

The doctor joined us and I was immediately impressed with him. He was very precise and to the point in his commentary and was obviously very sharp. His descriptions of the operation was highlighted by the following points:

* I would need a complete physical exam by my family doctor to ensure that I would most likely not suffer any complications during the surgery;
* I would have to complete a series of tests conducted by a neuropsychologists and other specialists whose titles I probably couldn't spell.

CHAPTER TEN

The Waiting Game

(DBS MINUS ONE DAY)

I've got a case of "day-before blues." It's a day when you have a lot of time on your hands. The waiting is probably worse than the actual event, which is called Deep Brain Stimulation in the subthalamus.

That means it is quite deep in the brain, and not that simple or routine an operation.

It's interesting that they will allow me to be conscious throughout the surgical procedure... except when they are fitting a head holding device on my skull.

I've got a case of day-before blues. I've got news for you. The day before a major operation is one of the worst days of your life. I can't imagine how difficult it must be for a cancer patient. You don't know whether to button up your life and prepare for the worst or assume that everything will go well and your life will move back to "Forward" rather than "hold". It's just not a great day to buy green bananas.

The waiting is difficult, because I really don't know what to expect tomorrow as the doors of O.R. swing open to me. Waiting that day was similar to the waiting I did the day before I was married and the day before our first son was born. While I wait, I decided to call a number of my friends and business associates to let them know what I'm getting myself into. I didn't reach even one of them. Unfortunately, I talked to all of their Voice Mails. Still, I'm waiting… and waiting…

If it were written as a song, I might write it like this:

OH, BABY, I'VE GOT THE DAY-BEFORE BLUES
AND I'M READY WITH MY HAT, MY PIN STRIPED SUIT, AND MY
BLUE SUEDE SHOES.
OH BABY, LET'S TAKE TO THE STREETS AND SING
LET'S GO BABY, I'VE GOT THE EVER-LOVIN,
BABY IN THE OVEN,
STOP THE PUSHIN AND THE SHOVIN
DAY-BEFORE BLUES

WO - WO - WO

At this point, there's no turning back. Let me tell you, though, that turning back is not my nature. I very rarely stop what I am doing and turn back. But the waiting is excruciating. I can't focus on any particular subject or project.

I am so anxious to get on with the surgery that I feel distracted, and I keep thinking about that operating room and the doctor with his big knife and drill, ready to carve up my brain into a bunch of little brains. When they wheel me back into the recovery room, will I be whole or in parts?

I spent part of the day online, part of it watching football and munching chips, part of it looking at available apartments in Birmingham. Luckily, the World Series is on tonight on TV, or I might be climbing the walls.

I dug out the sweatpants I want to wear to the hospital tomorrow. Nancy suggests that I take a small gym bag with a minimum of contents, so I don't have to drag a lot of stuff home after recovery. (Mental Note: Don't forget to take along a clean baseball or golf hat. End of Mental Note.)

Everything in my life is on hold, pending surgery results. I am hoping those results will put us back in charge of our lives, but we'll just have to play the game one day at a time.

> *OH, BABY, I'VE GOT THE EVER-LOVIN,*
> *Push and shovin'*
> *Turtle doven*
> *Day-Before Blues*
> *MY.......MY*

And think of something else besides the damned operation. There'll be plenty of time to think about that tomorrow.

CHAPTER ELEVEN

The Memorable Day

One of the bits of good luck that Nancy and I encountered in this scenario is not having to be at the hospital at the crack of dawn. It's always difficult for us to get going at 3:30 or 4 a.m., no matter how important the appointment might be.

This one is huge. We have surgery scheduled today with one of the nation's finest and most respected surgeons and his team. We were scheduled to show up at the hospital at 10 a.m., and that's about when Nancy swung our Dodge mini van into the Valet Parking drop-off point at William Beaumont hospital, where the surgery would be done. Today, there would be two DBS surgeries, a very unusual workload for both the surgeon and his staff.

If facilities mean anything in surgery, these get extremely high marks compared to other hospitals I have experienced.

At Beaumont, you won't see a lot of patients on gurneys in the aisles as at other hospitals. In fact, you won't see much of anything in the aisles, because they schedule their tests, and deliver their patient in time for the test. When the test is over, someone is there to pick up the gurney and return the patient to his room or back to the O.R., as in my case. When we arrived at the hospital, Nancy and I were greeted by our granddaughter Kayla and her mom as they were preparing to leave. Coincidentally, she had had some tubes inserted in her ears the same day of my surgery. She wished us well and left for home. I wished I could have done the same.

We were directed to the pre-op waiting room, which is close to the operating room. A large crowd of people populated the waiting room. At various times, families were called to the desk, where doctors or nurses would update them on the condition of their loved ones. I heard nothing but glowing reports on the morning surgeries. Good news!

After a few minutes of watching these scenes repeat themselves, we met the most delightful twin ladies from Birmingham. There was no mistaking the fact that they were identical twins. One of them was in to have her knees checked after recent surgery, and Nancy struck up a conversation with them.

Unfortunately, one of the twins had packed a bagel in her bag and they were consuming it while we talked. My stomach was empty, and I would have given a king's ransom for a couple of bites, but I had to maintain the fast.

Soon it was time to head into pre-op, and I sat with Jeannie Draggoo, the head nurse, who explained the process to me one more time. Among other topics was the use of a catheter because of the length of the operation. I certainly didn't look forward to its installation. The last time I was at Beaumont, I had a catheter attached to my penis for more than a week.

A battery of nurses got me dressed properly and ready for inspection by Nurse Draggoo. I had white stockings up and over my knees, and short light blue socks to keep my feet warm.

The surgeon was Dr. Fred Junn, assisted by Dr. John Hamilton, and Dr. Ken Jenrow, Ph.D., resident with the neurosurgery department at Henry Ford Hospital, and Susan Zachmann, research assistant. They are all strong, independent individuals, but together they are dynamite. I am Number 16 on their list of patients to be dealt with during this particular cycle. Dr. Junn had performed the Deep Brain Stimulation operations a number of times in Canada before he brought it to the United States, and it is still considered experimental here. Ten weeks after my surgery, the use of DBS as the sanctioned Parkinson's surgery was approved by the FDA. The label of "experimental" should be removed, and a label titled "outstanding" added, as far as I am concerned.

My first encounter is with Dr. Hamilton, Susan, Jeanne, and Dr. Junn, who collectively assemble and place the head frame after Drr. Junn numbs my head. (Some of my wise guy friends would say that my head has been numb for a long time. **Watch** it!) The head frame comes in a sealed package that is unpacked by Dr. Hamilton. He reminded me of a professional pool player as he meticulously laid out each piece onto a sterile blue cloth. Using the nuts and bolts provided, he assembles the main unit and slides it over your head. Then he starts screwing the unit into your skull. I said **into** your skull.After he had it all put together, he called Dr. Junn for an inspection. Unfortunately, he didn't approve of the way it had been put together and ordered Dr. Hamilton to take it apart and do it again. Accordingly, the doctor followed instructions and the headgear was more comfortably repositioned to Dr. Junn's satisfaction. After the head frame is secured, they put me in a wheel chair and took me to the Magnetic Resonance Imaging room within

Radiology, where I spent the next hour. First, they add a few unwelcome pieces to the head halo. This experience is one that I will remember vividly, but I don't ever want to do it again.

For what seems to be an interminable hour, you are lying flat on your back, listening to very abrasive and loud sounds of the machine that are not soothing in any way. I guess the closest experience to an MRI would be putting your head into a metal bucket and having someone pound on it with a metal hammer. It's metal on metal, and they have four screws that hold the frame in place with a lot of pressure from the screws on your skull. You have a blue panic switch to squeeze if you get claustrophobic or become ill. I didn't have to use mine, but I was close several times.

The chamber has a little lighting, but not enough to keep you awake. Actually, you're better off sleeping, because the time will pass far more quickly. When your eyes are open, there's nothing to see, so you may as well catch some zzz's. You begin to think you're gong to go bonkers, but you hear the technician in charge indicate the conclusion of the MRI, and shuts off the machine. He then calls one of the male nurses, who assists him in shoveling you onto a large flat board. Then they slide your dead weight onto your own bed and you begin the trip to the O.R. The only scenery you witness is ceilings. I suppose there are many things you can do when you're enroute to O.R. on a gurney. I prayed.

What little hair I had left on my head fluttered in the breeze created by the rapid movement of the gurney.

As I reentered the O.R., I noticed that a much larger group of people was there to meet me. I counted ten staff members, including the main man, Dr. Junn. In order to probe the inside of your head, an incision is made on both sides of the top of your scalp and a hole is drilled through the skull in order to be able to send an electrode down to determine where the deep brain stimulator will be placed. Some light anesthesia is provided at this point to make the drilling tolerable. When you awaken,

Dr. Junn is ready to begin operating on your brain. In a few moments, the Big Event began. Cue the trumpets.

Periodically, the doctor lectures the staff on issues of consequence in the operation. He was particularly upset this time about the disarrangement of some tools that he needed for the surgery, and let them know that he wanted things done his way. They all seemed to agree with him.

I noticed a unique phenomenon during the operation.

When things are seemingly going well, the staff members tend to congregate in clumps and chit chat on a variety of subjects, some related to the operation and others not. But when things are not all that great, they tend to separate and you hear very little chitter-chatter. When things get a little scary, they clam up and watch the surgeon perform. As you might imagine, a lot of chatter is very comforting.

One constant in the Operating Room is Jeanne Draggoo, R.N. She is always on top of things and makes sure that the doctor is well served. At one point, he asked for a "snake like" thing with a strange sort of end on it, and Jeanne went out of O.R. in search of this gadget. In 15 minutes or so, she was back with another one of her team members, and had the doohicky in her hand.

Jeanne is also the patient's best friend in O.R. She updates the patient on progress with winks and "thumbs up" signals that mean a great deal to the patient. Jeanne holds the project together. She is the glue that bonds the team together, and the chief cheerleader.

In my estimation, she is also a peach of a woman.

Another constant is the beeping of the EKG machine that reports your pulse and heart beat, so they can all listen to you get excited or remain relaxed. Mine stayed relatively stable throughout the surgery.

As the operation proceeds, Dr. Junn identifies the electrodes he is working on and gets confirmation from Dr. Jenrow. This is the process known as mapping. The electrode is sent down into the brain to a certain level and when it is reached, the patient is given a bit of electical stimulation. If the stimulation is felt somewhere on the patient's body, the patient must tell Dr. Jenrow at that precise time. This information is then recorded on electronic equipment, and it provides Dr. Junn with just the information he requires, enabling him to implant the electrodes precisely and accurately. My main question throughout the procedure was "how far we have gone since the start of the operation?" I wanted to know whether we were 20% or 50% home, and Dr. Junn kept me apprised of his progress.

After both stimulators are implanted, the frame is removed from the head and the patient is taken to the recovery room and monitored for any signs of deterioration. The next move is to the general neurosurgery unit, where the patient is carefully watchd. The next day, another MRI is performed to make sure there is no hemorrhage from the surgery. Everything was perfect in my case.

Thankfully, there is no head frame and the MRI is a lot shorter than it was the day before.

While the operating team is working over you, there are several key risk areas they are watching with considerable interest. They include bleeding inside the brain; leakage of fluid surrounding the brain; seizure; and infection. Any of the four could drastically affect your results. Dr. Junn told us that he once lost a patient who hemorraged, but the procedure was not for Parkinson's correction, so I dismissed the possibility that it could happen to me.

Nurse Draggoo does test stimulations the next day by using a hand held device, since the Pulse generators are not implanted until the following week. This post-test gives Dr. Junn an indication that the stimulators are working and that a threshhold and a top limit of stimulation can be achieved. The patient will go home the next day and come back to the hospital the following week for insertion of the pulse generators.

The pulse generators are about 2 inches in diameter, and they are implanted under your skin, below your collarbone. In my case, I have two of these gadgets—one for each side of my brain. When the brain swelling subsides, Nurse Dragoo introduces a brief case with lots of meters and electrical hardware inside. With this unit, she was able to program my system and get it operational. At this initial session, it was decided to keep the intensity of our system low while we elected to reduce the medications.

I was constantly tested during this session. When Dr. Trosch performed the final tests, he said that fine tuning the program could take up to a full year. As long as improvement is demonstrated, I don't care if it takes five years. It is so much better than before. I can only say "thanks" to everyone that made it happen.

In the weeks that followed, people around me remarked that I was much more animated than before. The "Parkinson's Mask" that I was saddled with before was gone, and I was back to my old self again. I looked at Nancy, and she breathed a sigh of relief. It felt so good to be almost normal again.

The initial programming of the deep brain stimulators is completed after swelling is reduced, preventing any chance for false parameters to be set.

Periodic followup is determined at that time and medications are adjusted by the patient's neurologist. In my case, I have eliminated completely two of the medications, Comtan and Amantadine. Also, I have reduced Sinemet and Permax to about half of what I had been taking.

Is there any wonder that I feel we have turned my life around?

CHAPTER TWELVE

Life on the Line

How would you like a job that put your customers' lives on the line every day? That's the way life is for members of the team that works with Dr. Junn in the O.R. They do one patient per normal week, but the day I was scheduled for surgery, they performed two operations. But several equipment breakdowns convinced them that two was one too many, they said afterward.

The doctor who performed the surgery is Dr. Fred Junn, a Detroit-area surgeon who came to the U.S. by way of Canada. He has an M.D. from the University of Western Ontario and took advanced training at the University of Toronto. His Board Certification is through the Royal College of Physicians and Surgeons of Canada.

His special medical interests include Parkinson's disease and other movement disorders such as tremors, dystonia, torticollis, and spasticity.

His research interests focus on peripheral nerve repair and reconstruction, understanding human motor circuit physiology underlying movement disorders, stroke induced movement and pain disorders. Dr.Junn has performed more Deep Brain Stimulation operations than all of the neurosurgeons in Michigan combined. He works at Henry Ford hospital, and performs some of his surgeries at Willliam Beaumont hospital in Royal Oak, Michigan.

Jeanne Draggoo, RN, graduated from the University of Cincinnati Raymond Walters School of Nursing in 1979,followed by 15 years of employment by the the University Hospital mostly in the neurosurgery/neurology departments. In her last five years at U.C., her practice focused on movement disorders.

After relocating to Michigan, Nurse Draggoo joined the neurology department at

Henry Ford hospital in Detroit and is currently Nurse Coordinator of the movement disorder surgery program with Dr. Junn.

She is a member of the American Association of Neuroscience Nurses and is licensed in the states of Michigan and Ohio to practice nursing.

With credentials like these, both Dr. Junn and Nurse Draggoo made me feel very comfortable about my chances of coming out of surgery with all of our objectives accomplished. And we have.

CHAPTER THIRTEEN

A New Beginning

It's all over and we have survived! I was rolled out of the Operating Room at about 9:20 p.m., six hours after we entered the O.R. I was awake and aware that I had overcome one of the greatest challenges of my life. They put me off to one corner of the Recovery Room. It was unusual for surgery to be performed so late, so I was the only one there.

I felt so hungry I could eat a blanket, so I called the nurse and explained that I had not eaten anything since midnight the previous day and that it would be a good idea to get some soup or something into my stomach. Also, I had had no medications for over 24 hours.

My first encounter with her was not terribly encouraging. She was a confrontational type of personality, and indicated that she would be in charge for the next four hours, and things would be her way or the highway. I wasn't in a very argumentative mood, but I presented my case in a logical way... but to no avail.

The nurse was somewhat preoccupied by a test that evidently had been distributed earlier in the day. She and other nurses discussed, ad infinitum, the questions on the test. As a result, I learned more about nursing that evening than I ever wanted to know.

When the backup nurse, Margaret, came on duty as Sue took a break, I worked her over for food and meds as well. I told her that I had brought my own medications to the hospital and directed her to the pills, but she insisted on ordering meds from the hospital pharmacy.

This idea seemed ludicrous to me as I lay helpless on the bed in the recovery room. After all, who would better know what to take better than I? By ordering it from the pharmacy, they were creating opportunities for errors in dosage, strength of medications, and so on.

There are now two metal stimulators in my chest, the result of a rather routine operation that took place last Monday, just a week after the doctor had attached electrodes in my brain. Now I was ready for the programming and plug-in phases, which would take place two weeks later. During that two week period, I noticed that my condition was worse than it had ever been. I couldn't get up from a chair without help, I couldn't get dressed in the morning without help, and I couldn't move once I was positioned in bed at night. Therefore, I looked forward eagerly to the plug-in process, hoping that all of those shortcomings would be alleviated.

About two weeks after the surgery, I was programmed by Nurse Draggoo.

The nurse explained that the brain swells during the surgery, and no programming can take place until the swelling subsides, normally two weeks following the operation. Unfortunately, there were some tense moments during that two week period when I assumed it wasn't working and that we had wasted our time... and I'd have to live with the condition. But I didn't let thoughts like that linger around too long, and it all began to take shape after the second "tune up"session, when she calibrated my setting at 2.6 vs. 1.5 the first week. At 2.6, I could function on half the pills I had been taking, and so I reduced the medications to 12 from 21. The impact was that the system took over and furnished the stimulation demanded by my brain.

CHAPTER FOURTEEN

Along for the Treacherous Ride
By Nancy Knitter

My days prior to Harry's DBS surgery were like a roller coaster at an amusement park. Each day over the past four years was an unknown phenomenon. Sometimes within the same day, his condition would change, depending upon whether his medications had "kicked in" or not. Just when things appear to be on an even keel, and I started to relax, something happened to send me into a downward spiral.

It has been almost ten years since the neurologist diagnosed Harry with Parkinson's Disease. The first five years were the "honeymoon years," with just a few complications that were resolved with a small amount of medication.

On the day he first told me that the doctor diagnosed him as a Parkinsonian, I wasn't shocked or stunned; I just couldn't believe him. I didn't know what lied ahead of us. We checked out our families and none of them had exhibited Parkinson's symptoms. So I gathered as much information as I could, and he went on with his career, never seeming to want to know more about the disease than he had to. My husband felt that the doctor would tell him about any new developments along the way. (Note: Dig out as much information as you can from the library, where you'll find a lot of books on the subject; also on internet, where you will find groups and individuals qualified to tell you what you want to know.)

Do not rely only on the neurologist to keep you posted. Their time with you is limited, and that is not their main concern. The neurologist we work with now IS concerned about side effects of meds and quality of life issues because he specializes in movement disorders.

Our marriage for the first 38 years had been a good one, and our relationship was solid, loving, and supportive. Oh, we dealt with the usual challenges involved in child raising (three sons) and job changes, relocations, and the like. But we truly enjoyed each other's company and did most things together.

Our interests are similar. We enjoy sports, music, art, travel, and people. He is very gregarious, and will start up a conversation almost anywhere, any time.

My husband can find out about the person he is sitting next to better than almost anyone I know of. He introduces himself, talks about the books he has written, and in minutes has a complete profile on the person who was a total stranger just minutes ago.

Harry is strong willed and used to doing things his way in business dealings. Therefore, it was no suprise that he would deal with Parkinson's in the same way. There is no way he would allow the disease to get the best of him. I have always been exceedingly proud of him. However, considerable friction emerged in our relationship when his personality changed as medications were increased and dosages expanded.

How could someone change so drastically from his previous personality? I addressed the issue with the head of neurology at our state's osteopathic school of medicine, but didn't get anywhere. He took the position that side effects were not part of his responsibility, after he had prescribed the medicine in question.

A short time after taking his mid morning dose, Harry would ride high, doing things he couldn't do earlier. But he also became abrupt, somewhat obnoxious, and he would disappear for hours and then lie about what he was doing during that time.

(Note: Get a lot of information about your neurologist before you commit to one particular doctor. Try to find a movement or Parkinson's specialist. If we had done that, we would have saved three years of emotional problems that have taken a toll on my mental and physical health.)

My husband lost his job in the corporate world after an exemplary career. Even though his associates knew he suffered from Parkinson's disease, they didn't bother to find out more about it or make him aware of the personality changes they had observed. They dismissed him, not concerning themselves with the trauma they would cause, compounding the existing problems. In another situation, a good friend saw her husband demoted by a large insurance firm, his company car taken away, and he was reassigned to a desk job that he was not trained for at headquarters, all because of his Parkinson's affliction. I am sure there are other stories like these in the unfeeling corporate world. I have heard of a couple of exceptions of companies such as Dow and EDS that have worked with the afflicted, but valued employee, in restructuring their work load.

I would suggest that you share your concerns with your family. Help them understand what you are going through and solicit their help, if you can. I failed to do that, and I regret my omission. I tried to keep them out of our problems because they had their own challenges to look after. For some, a support group may be very helpful, because you will have someone outside of your own world to talk with and share information. Just talking with others who know what you are going through is very therapeutic.

I like being called Care Partner because I am working with him when he needs me. After all, I was not trained to be a Care Giver. When he needs his pants hiked up or buttoned when we are out, I give him a hug before and after I fix his pants. And then I add a kiss. Sometimes people around us think we are sharing a romantic moment, but we really are handling a button or a "hike" of his pants. He loves the hug and kiss routine.

I try to help him maintain his dignity as much as possible. That's not always easy, when you need to dab the drool from his chin or help him get in and out of bed, or take over driving when his medications prevent him from driving safely. I was lucky that his condition was not as bad as some others we have seen at the seminars, and I can bet you that as frustrated as the patient is, the Care Partner shares the same frustration, pain, and humiliation, especially if the Care Partner is a spouse.

Luckily, our marriage has been strong, built on mutual faith we shared from the very beginning. I was determined that this disease would not kill our marriage. I could deal with his physical needs, but his mental problems almost did me in. The damn pills and their side effects practically tore us apart. Our neurologist told us that many patients experience different reactions to their prescriptions. Men with Parkinson's seem to experience compulsive behaviors more frequently than women.

When the opportunity to have DBS surgery came up, it was like a lifeline was being thrown to a floundering swimmer. We knew that his rigidity and dyskensia were worsening, and that more medication would be needed. From the first meeting with Dr. Junn, however, we were impressed with the team that would handle the operation. Harry would have gone to the hospital that day if he could have.

We found out that his condition actually worsened after the surgery, but the setback was temporary and probably caused by the swelling of the brain. After about two weeks, we knew we just had to be patient.

Since the DBS surgery, our life seems much better controlled. He has reduced his intake of medications to about 50% of the level prior to the operation. Although his condition fluctuates each day, the range of highs and lows is much more compressed than before. His hardware has been programmed twice, and may require adjustments for up to a year, according to Dr. Trosch.

In the meantime, I feel the operation was successful. We both understand that Harry is a "work in progress" patient, and that we have to continue to stay on top of all the new research.

When we had our third consultation with Nurse Draggoo, the intensity of the system was turned up one notch, to 2.6 on a 3.5 scale. At the same time, Harry mentioned to Dr. Trosch that he has cut out Comtan AND Amantadine completely. We're already down by 50% in our Permax and Sinemet intake, and we'll begin to work on reducing those medications further as time goes by.

I have no doubt that a cure will be discovered in the next ten years, and that future Parkinsonians will have a much easier time of it. People like Muhammed Ali and Michael J. Fox are making a concerted effort to raise the funds that are needed for research. It appears a cure is within our grasp NOW. Harry and I are just regular,small town people, but we hope our story will help provide others with useful information. Whatever you do, remember: you are never alone, so don't ever give up.

CHAPTER FIFTEEN

Frequently Asked Questions

Q1. <u>Aren't you premature in saying that you have "beat"Parkinson's?</u>

Based on what I've heard and seen and felt, this procedure reverses the symptoms and eliminates most of them. That's good enough for me. I've got the bastard licked, and I am never going back to the miseries of the past. I hate everything the disease brings to innocent people who want to live out their lives peacefully and independently.

Q2. <u>Aren't you constantly worried that something will stop your sending units and screw up your system?</u>

I haven't heard of any consistent problem. The ones I have are the latest version of the units, and they appear to be working well. If I turn off the stimulators, I have to have medication. It's just either... or. What could be simpler?

I've been told that I don't have to worry if I stay away from airport x-ray machines, real strong microwaves, and green-eyed redheads. They all stress out my system.

We use the most ridiculous system to test whether the units are on or not. I have bought several $5.00 Kmart radios, and we turn them down to the low end of the AM settings.

Then we press the radios against my senders (pacemakers), and the level of static tells us whether they are "ON"or not. Medtronic is the developer of a unit to achieve the same end result, but has not received final approval. We learned about this from a couple we met in the doctor's waiting room. And you thought you knew everything.

Q3. <u>This is an awfully expensive procedure. At $70,000, it's making some people extremely rich.</u>

I know I haven't communicated to you the precise knowledge, the steady hands, the wonderful expertise that is activated by your own inertia. If I didn't have the money to have this done, I would get it. "Oh, Uncle Jake, I wanted to talk to you......" We all have ways of getting important things done. What's more important than this?

There are always some ways to collect $70,000.

Q4. <u>My grandfather had Parkinson's. Does that mean I will probably get the disease when I'm older?</u>

A. Not necessarily. You just can't predict where and when the disease will strike. Most patients are over 50 and it affects females as well as males. It is estimated that about a half million people are walking around with the disease but that it has not been diagnosed.

If you observe or experience the symptoms, be sure you see your neurologist early.

There is no way to know how much heredity plays a role in P.D. Most cases are thought to be caused by both environmenta and genetic factors.

Q5: <u>Are there other forms of surgery besides DBS?</u>

None of the currently known surgical approaches really cures the disease, but several methods have helped patients lead more satisfying lives. Pallidotomy is a way to reduce dyskinesia caused by medication. A tiny hole is drilled in the skull and with an electric probe, the surgeon destroys a sall part of the global pallidus, which is believed to be overactive in a Parkinson's patient. See Chapter 15 for more information.

Q6. <u>Have you encountered myths about Parkinson's that are not necessarily true?</u>

A. Yes. The first one is that the disease is fatal. I suppose you could say that if you were crossing the street slowly, and got hit by a car. But there is nothing fatal about the disease itself.

The second one has to do with dementia. Since the disease affects older people, outsiders conclude that the Parkinsonians slow up mentally. I'll admit that I don't think as clearly as I once did. But as Dr. Trosch has reminded me, it's not due to P.D. It's due to age. End of story.

One other myth: Your medications will lose power over time. Baloney. They will maintain the same level of potency, but your body will require more as you age. That's why DBS is so good. It will fill in the gap and keep you from taking large doses of medicine in your latter years.

Q7. <u>What's the best way to find a good neurologist?</u>

Go to support group meetings and seminars and talk to people. Find out who's satisfied with their doctor and why. Find out which neurologist schedules fewer patients than the others so he can spend a lot of time with you, rather than rushing through an inconclusive discussion. Find out who is getting the majority of all patients, who does more than just dispense meds, and who seems to really care about you. That's your man or woman!

Q8. <u>Do only old people get Parkinson's?</u>

A. While at the neurologist's office, my wife and I met a fellow who had the disease at 28 and has been battling it for 13 years. He has a family to support. So younger people need to be concerned that it may strike just about anyone. Michael J. Fox was in his thirties when he contracted the disease.

Q9. <u>What about depression? Weren't you depressed when you were going downhill?</u>

A. There's no room in my life for depression. I like to think positive and I don't let myself get down. Parkinson's tests you every day but I made up my mind early, and it was to not allow Parkinson's to beat me. I also pledged that defeat was unacceptable.

Q10. <u>You mentioned that you and your wife attended many seminars in the past ten years. Are some better than others?</u>

A. The benefits you receive are almost always directly related to the quality of the speaker. And since many of the speakers are doctors, who have little time to prepare speeches, the presentations are often over our heads and in doc-speak. There have been a lot of upside-down slides, too.

To me, the value of a seminar is watching the audience assemble and depart. Here you'll find Parkinsonians of all ages, and more importantly, all conditions. I always try to find that feeble patient who is so far along, I don't ever want to reach that point.

If your group can't find a speaker, call me at 888-567-3363. I'm always glad to share my message with anyone who is interested in the topic of dealing with Parkinson's. And the small fee I charge goes directly to the National Parkinson's Foundation. After all, if we don't stop to help one another, who will do it?

Q11: <u>What are my chances in dealing with Parkinson's Disease if I don't have health insurance?</u>

A. You have a big problem. The medications I take cost result in a co-pay of between $20 and $4.00. Our average cost per month, after insurance, is about $64.00. The surgery cost was totally covered. We estimate that if I didn't have insurance, the cost to maintain my present condition would average out to $800 per month. That's a lot of bucks for the average guy. I've got a better idea: buy books and keep me off the streets.

Q12: <u>Can you suggest some ways to make life easier for the person with Parkinson's?</u>

A: Yes. For heaven's sake, get a Handicapped hanger card for your car. Don't pass up an opportunity to park with plenty of space around you to help get in and out of your car.

Next, don't put yourself in a position of jeopardy. If there is no reason to grocery shop at 6 p.m. Friday, don't do it. Shop at 2 p.m. Monday, if that's a down time.

Travel around town when everyone else isn't, and you'll be much more comfortable and confident that you can handle it.

Third, wear clothing that's easy to get on and off. You know that dressing yourself is a major challenge, so make it easy on yourself by pre-planning.

Q13. <u>Who are some of the better known people who have had to put up with Parkinson's?</u>

A. Probably the most active and supportive person is Michael J. Fox, who has a lot of dyskenisia, so he has dropped out of the cast of his TV show. Others are:Morris Udall, Janet Reno, Muhammed Ali (his affliction is called "Parkinson's Syndrome") Johnny Cash, Billy Graham, and British Actor Terri Thomas.

Q14. <u>What about sleeping and eating. Any difficulties?</u>

A. I have commented about sleeping. I don't get much out of it, and I try to get up each day by 5:30 or so. I know that my body needs it, but, to me, it is a waste of time. I prefer to work and be productive.

As far as eating is concerned, when do you want to go to lunch? I specialize in cheeseburgers, and they go down very smoothly, with or without barium.

CHAPTER SIXTEEN

Making Life Easier

If you have Parkinson's, try to make life a little easier by doing a few simple little things. First of all, by all means get a Handicapped hanger card for your car. You'll shortcut a lot of parking problems and open up some space around your car when you get in and out.

When you walk, take long strides and avoid the shuffle routine. You'll find yourself feeling a lot better about your condition if you walk fairly normally.

When you buy shoes, get the type with Velcro tops rather than shoe strings. Wear sweat suits with elastic bottoms, so you won't need suspenders.

Wear clothes with elastic fronts and wear workout jackets instead of sweaters. They are much easier to get in and out of.

When you speak, look the other person squarely in the face. Speak louder than normal, and don't let others speak for you. Practice speaking in private and read out loud, so your voice will be exercised.

If your speech problem is troublesome, consult a speech therapist or pathologist for treatment.

Don't forget to exercise your mind. Participate in senior center activities. Read. Go to movies. Live life as if life is short, because it is!

Don't let Parkinson's stand in your way any more than necessary. Take your medication and live your life as normally as you can, for there won't be any second chances.

In the coming years, when they finally find a cure, you will be ready to take advantage of it, and it's going to be a wonderful day.

CHAPTER SEVENTEEN

Mother and DBS

Janet Leonard, whose mother has had PD since she was 40, described her experience with DBS in detail. Here is her report:

First, a bit of background. My mother had symptoms for several years before a diagnosis of PD was made. She was approximately 40 years old when diagnosed and at that time there was no medication to treat PD symptoms. Shortly thereafter, L-Dopa was introduced. Although it helped the PD symptoms and was almost like a miracle because she could move, the side effects were awful and she threw up every day for two years. Then, Sinemet was introduced and controlled her symptoms effectively for many years.

As the years wore on, and the disease progressed, she began to slowly lose the effectiveness of her medication. She tried all the agonists out there including Mirapex, Requip, Comtan, etc., but none seemed to help and with some there were side effects.

After much reading up on the subject I decided that we needed to pursue surgery as an option, either a pallidotomy or Deep Brain Stimulation surgery (DBS). At first my mother was dead set against it, but I convinced her to at least go and see what they had to say. The first neurosurgeon had never done DBS in the subthalamus, which controls all the symptoms of PD. DBS in the thalamus has been much more widely performed but treats tremor only. My mother had bilateral symptoms including on/off periods, hot and cold feelings, stiffness, rigidity, freezing and moderate tremor. We decided to consult a neurosurgeon who had experience with DBS in the subthalamus.

We decided upon a Dr. Jeffrey Arle, a neurosurgeon at the Lahey Clinic in Burlington, MA. He explained the procedure but kind of underplayed it a little, made it seem less involved than it was. Before you can be considered a candidate, you have to go through some pre-testing. This includes blood work, chest x-ray, MRI of the brain, and for older patients (my mother was 73) approximately 4 hours of neurophychological testing to make sure she had no significant memory loss. The surgery can made memory loss worse. All these tests took a lot out of her but I told her if they find you are a candidate then you have a decision to make, if not then you know it is not an option. I would encourage everyone who is seriously considering this surgery to have the pre-tests to make sure you are a candidate.

The date of the surgery was August 2, 2000. She went in that morning and they want you to be completely off your medication for the surgery. They originally asked her to stop it the night before but we said it would be impossible to get her dressed and to the hospital after being off meds that long. They told her she could have her 6 a.m. meds but nothing after that. The surgery was set for 9 a.m.

You are brought into a room where a catheter is inserted into your bladder and a halo (large metal frame) is attached to the head and can be painful. Then the biggest mistake we made because we were uninformed happened. My mother was brought out of anesthesia for the drilling into the scalp. She said it was like a bomb went off in her head and she saw black and colored specks. She thought she had gone blind, which of course she had not. The drilling while she was awake still haunts her and I would strongly encourage anyone planning on going through this surgery to INSIST that they be put out on anesthetics during the drilling into the scalp and the scraping of the tunnels where the wires will lay. Her doctor has since changed his policy and now does not wake up his patients until this phase is done. He changed his policy because of my mother's bad reaction and fears.

Once awakened, the patient is unable to move, partly because of being off meds and partly because of the iron cage halo. Then the doctors locate the best area to insert the electrode. This location is best found by the use of microrecordings which some hospitals and some do not. From what I have read, it is very important to use the microrecordings to assure you are getting the best possible placement of the electrode for the best possible result. The surgery for one side took four to five hours. They do put current to the electrode during surgery and ask the patient to move their leg, noting whether they can control tremors and other symptoms to assure they have the right location. The patient is then sewn up and sent to the Recovery Room.

I would suggest that you find out in advance whether the hospital uses generic Sinemet, as was the case with my mother's hospital. If they do, and generic Sinemet does not work on you, make arrangements beforehand with your doctor or the hospital staff that you will bring and use your own medication. They usually insist that it be in a marked bottle from the pharmacy. This is very important to the patients who can't take generic meds. After the procedure is done and you are finally able to take your med, the last thing you want is to get Sinemet that is not going to work.

My mother is one of 20% of PD patients who are protein sensitive. This means that if she eats protein around the time when she takes her medication, her medication will not work. The protein in these patients blocks the absorption of the Sinemet. She is also one of the few patients that can not take generic Sinemet; it just does not work on her. That is what they gave her in the hospital so while she was in the recovery room they were giving her the generic meds so she was stiff and more uncomfortable than need be. I thought I would mention these points in case they would help someone by trying to take your meds without a meal with protein, to determine whether you are protein sensitive. Also, if meds aren't working properly, try brand name drugs to see if you are provided with relief.

Once we got her brand name Sinemet to her she seemed fine, really wiped out from the surgery, but she did go home the following day. She seemed to have a period of depression after the surgery. Some doctors turn the stimulators on the next day, but our surgeon said it was best to wait two weeks for the brain swelling to subside. He said that turning it on too soon results in more visits to have the stimulators adjusted and a greater probability of dyskenesia. He recommends having one side done at a time. He feels it is too much for the patient and the doctor to do two sides in one day and after seeing what my mother went through I would agree. Perhaps someone younger could tolerate the procedure on both sides. This surgeon recommends a month between surgeries.

My mother was so traumatized by the drilling and being awake all the time that she would not consent to having the other stimulator implanted, even though she had symptoms on both sides and the doctor told us that one stimulator would not work because one side would be overstimulated and we would never get a good balanced result.

Unfortunately, we ran into a complication. Whether it was caused by the surgery or not we will never know. My mother had headaches during the days after surgery, and kept saying that she felt "weird". When I asked her what she meant, she couldn't explain it. The combination of electrodes, wires behind the ear, and stimulators just felt unnatural to her, I guess.

Eleven days after the surgery, she became unresponsive and my father brought her back to the hospital. A CAT SCAN determined that she had a brain bleed, with blood clots, on the opposite side of her brain, not the side the surgery was performed on. No one could understand it, since the brain is protected by a thick membrane that divides one side from the other. Still, they could not totally dismiss the coincidence that this had happened, nor could they totally convince us or themselves that it was not related to the surgery.

After the blood clots were removed, my mother had to make a slow recovery and wound up in the hospitals and rehabs for about six weeks. At first she was responsive, but very slowly came around and is back to about 95% of her normal functioning. I think she had some memory problems because of the blood clotting. Her condition is most evident when she is trying to take and remember taking her medications.

I read on "Ask Your Doctor" that 25% or patients benefit on both sides from one stimulator. We have been going back for four or five months to have the stimulator adjusted. It is not just a mattter of it being on or off. There are many variables. With the stimulators on, you need less medication, and it is a fine line between an ideal setting and too much or too little charge from the stimulators, so we just experiment at different levels.

It is a time consuming process, but she has gotten about 25% better from it. *Pills that used to last her two hours now last 3 to 4 hours. She is sleeping better at night and agrees that she feels better since the surgery. Yesterday, we set the stimulator at 2.6 from*

2.0, the biggest increase she has had since the electrodes were implanted. After taking Sinemet CR last night, she started getting dyskenesia.

So now we know that she is overmedicated and we can try experimenting with different combinations of Sinemet and stimulations in an attempt to find the balance we need in the equation. It becomes all trial and error.

Just remember when you consider this procedure that it is not a cure, but a treatment. You will still have off periods, but the bottom line is that patients who are at an impasse should consider going forward with the surgery.

If your meds are not effective any more, go for it. Just go into it with your eyes wide open.

I hope this information has helped clarify some of the issues and the ups and downs of the procedure. If you decide to do it, the most important thing is to be put asleep during the drilling into the skull and also make sure the doctor uses micro-recordings to assure the accurate placement of the electrodes and wires. My mom lives in Massachusetts and her doctor lives in Burlington, Massachusetts. I think he is a great guy, very calm, and a great surgeon. He is doing more and more of these every day. He told me recently that the procedure is now totally covered because it has received FDA approval.

I wish you success in your lousy battle against PD. I really do feel that we are on the cutting edge of a breakthrough in the treatment of PD. Just arm yourself with as much information as possible when you prepare for the operation.

Harry Knitter

Epilogue

I hope you have found this book difficult to put down. My approach to writing it was to make it as personal, yet informational, as possible. I hope I achieved that objective.

You'll find other books about Parkinson's that will also be more closely connected with the disease and its many facets.

What I have told you in this book is real, from my perspective, and there is nothing theoretical about it. Also, there is nothing so technical that you won't understand it. The focal point of the book is my surgery. If you have Parkinson's and can have the operation, go for it. You can always have additional surgery done later if some sort of improved version comes along. In the meantime, you'll get a lot more living out of life.

Today, I had my monthly checkup, and Nurse Draggoo intensified my impulses to 2.9 from 2.5, so I should be able to reduce my medications to about 50% of the level I was at before my operation. Dr. Trosch repeated his admonition that it may take a full year to adjust and fine tune the balance between my system and my meds. He said I should think of myself as a "work in progress." I agree with that, but only if I continue to improve from where I was just two months ago. SO FAR, SO GOOD.

Good luck, and remember: Life is short, so Never Give Up!

APPENDIX I

Who to Call

If you think you have Parkinson's symptoms, or have questions, the following Parkinson's centers can put you in touch with the people with answers. Contact them and seek out assistance.

ALABAMA

UNIVERSITY OF ALABAMA
AT BIRMINGHAM
Department of Neurology
1218 C.Jefferson Tower
Birmingham, AL 35294

(205) 934-9100

ARIZONA

PHOENIX

BARROW NEUROLOGICAL
INSTITUTE
350 WEST THOMAS ROAD
PHOENIX, AZ 85013

(602)285-6652

TUCSON

1650 EAST FORT LOWELL, SUITE 302
TUCSON, AZ 85719

(602) 326-3400

CALIFORNIA

IRVINE

UNIVERSITY OF IRVINE
DEPT. OF NEUROLOGY
107 IRVINE HALL
IRVINE, CA 92717

(714) 725-3500

USC SCHOOL OF MEDICINE
NATL. PARKINSON FOUNDATION
1510 San Pablo Street
Los Angeles, CA 90033

(800) 532-8855

NEWPORT BEACH

HOAG HOSPITAL
NATIONAL PARKINSON
FOUNDATION CENTER
355 Placentia
Newport Beach, CA.

(949)574-6338

LOS ANGELES

THE NEUROSCIENCE
INSTITUTE
HOSPITAL OF THE
GOOD SAMARITAN
637 South Lucas
Los Angeles, CA90017

(800) 841-8765

SAN DIEGO

4010 MORENA BLVD.
SUITE 224
SAN DIEGO, CA 92117

(619) 273-6763

RANCHO MIRAGE

EISENHOWER MEMORIAL
HOSPITAL
42201 BEACON HILL
PALM DESERT, CA 92260

(619) 773-3105

SAN FRANCISCO

SETON MEDICAL CENTER
1900 SULLIVAN AVE.
DALY CITY, CA 94015

Harry Knitter

(415) 991-6687
UNIV. OF CALIFORNIA,
SAN FRANCISCO
Parkinson's Disease Clinic
503 Parnassas Street
San Francisco, CA 94143

(415)476-9276

SAN DIEGO

UNIVERISTY OF CALIFORNIA, SAN DIEGO
DEPT. OF NEUROSCIENCES
9500 Gilman Driv
San Diego, CA 92093

(858) 545-8585

SANTA MARIA

APDA YOUNG PARKINSON'S INFORMATION
AND REFERRAL CENTER
1041 FOXENWOOD DRIVE
SANTA MARIA, CA 93455

(800) 223-9776

SUNNYVALE

THE PARKINSON'S INSTITUTE
1170 Morse Ave.
Sunnyvale, CA 94089

(408)734-2800

THE PARKINSON CENTER AT ST. JOHN'S
REGIONAL MEDICAL CENTER
The California Neuroscience Institute
1700 North Rose Ave.
Oxnard, CA 93930

(805) 988-7599

COLORADO

COLORADO NEUROLOGICAL INSTITUTE
300 EAST HAMPTON AVE.
ENGLEWOOD, CO 80110

(303) 781-5788

CONNECTICUT

HOSPITAL OF ST. RAPHAEL
SENIOR SERVICES
175 SHERMAN AVE.
NEW HAVEN, CT 06511

(203) 789-4289

DISTRICT OF COLUMBIA

GEORGETOWN UNIVERSITY
SCHOOL OF MEDICINE
3800 RESERVOIR ROAD
WASHINGTON, DC. 20007

(202) 687-5468

FLORIDA

University of Miami
Department of Neurology
1501 NW 9th Ave.

(800) 327-4545

NEUROMEDICAL RESEARCH
FOUNDATION, INC.
1135 KANE CONCOURSE
BAY HARBOR, FL 33154

(800) 825-2732

MOVEMENT DISORDERS
SOCIETY OF SOUTHWEST FLORIDA
Bank of America Building
126 E. Olympia,Avenue
Punta Gorda, FL 33950

(941) 833-8312

ST. PETERSBURG SUN
COAST CHAPTER
5970 80TH STREET NORTH
ST. PETERSBURG, FL 33709

(813) 544-2732

PARKINSON'S RESEARCH
CORPORATION
1207 Parilla
Tampa, FL 33613

(813) 968-9557

GEORGIA

EMORY UNIVERSITY SCHOOL OF MEDICINE
1365 CLIFTON RD., N.E.
ATLANTA, GA.30322

IDAHO

(404)248-5120

ST. ALPHONSUS MEDICAL CENTER
1055 NORTH CURTIS ROAD
BOISE, ID 83706

ILLINOIS

CENTER FOR HEALTH AGING
ST. JOSEPH HOSPITAL & HEALTH CENTER
2900 NORTH LAKESHORE DRIVE
CHICAGO, IL. 60657

(312) 975-3325

SOUTHERN ILLINOIS UNIVERSITY
Department of Neurology
P.O. Box 19643
Springfield, IL 62794

(217) 782-8249

KANSAS

KANSAS UNIVERSITY MEDICAL CENTER
Neuroloy Department
3901 Rainbow Blvd.
Kansas City, KS 66160

(913)588-6992

LOUISIANA

HOTEL DIEU HOSPITAL
2021 Perdio Street
New Orleans, LA 70112

(504) 588-3699

MARYLAND

JOHNS HOPKINS OUTPATIENT CENTER
DEPT. OF NEUROLOGY
601 N. Caroline St.
Baltimore, MD 21287'

MASSACHUSETTS

BOSTON UNIVERSITY SCHOOL OF MEDICINE
DEPT. OF NEUROLOGY
720 Harrison Ave.
Boston, MA 02118

617-6388-8466

MINNESOTA

METHODIST HOSPITAL
P.O. BOX 650
Minneapolis, MN 50022

(612) 932-5607

MONTANA

MONTANA DEACONNESS MEDICAL CENTER
1101 2nd st., South
Great Falls, MT 59405

(406) 455-5464

ST. MARY OF THE PLAINS HOSPITAL
4014 22ND PLACE
LUBBOCK, TX 79410

(806) 796-0689

MISSOURI

WASHINGTON UNIVERSITY
SCHOOL OF MEDICINE
660 EUCLID AVE.
ST. LOUIS, MO 63110

(314) 362-3299

NEW JERSEY

ROBERT WOOD JOHNSON UNIVERSITY HOSPITAL
1 Robert Wood Johnson Place
New Brunswick, NJ 08901

(908) 745-75 20

NEW YORK

FAR ROCKAWAY
PENINSULA HOSPITAL
51-15 Beach Channel Drive

Far Rockaway, NY 11691

(718) 945-7079

MANHATTAN

HOSPITAL OF JOINT DISEASES
Orthopedic Institute, Department of Nursing
301 East 17th St.
New York, NY 10003

OLD WESTBURY

NEW YORK COLLEGE OF OSTEOPATHIC MEDICINE
New York Institute of Technology
Old Westbury, NY 11568

ROCHESTER
The UNIVERSITY OF ROCHESTER
SCHOOL OF MEDICINE AND DENTISTRY
DEPARTMENT OF NEUROLOGY

601 Elmwood Avenue
Rochester,NY 14642

SMITHTOWN

ST. JOHN'S EPISCOPAL HOSPITAL
Route 25A
Smthtown, NY 11787

STATEN ISLAND

STATEN ISLAND UNIVERSITY
HOSPITAL
Ambulatory Pavilian
475 Seaview Avenue
Staten Island, NY 10305

(718) 226-6129

NORTH CAROLINA

DURHAM

DUKE SOUTH MEDICAL
CENTER
MPDC
Durham,NC 27710

(919) 681-2033

OHIO

UNIVERSITY OF CINCINNATI
MEDICAL CENTER

Harry Knitter

Charles D. Aring Center
234 Goodman Street
Cincinnati, Ohio 45267

(513) 558-6770

OKLAHOMA

TULSA

Hillcrest Medical Center System
3220 South Peoria
Tulsa, OK 74105

(918) 747-3747

OREGON

OREGON HEALTH SCIENCES UNIVERSITY
DEPT. OF NEUROLOGY
3181 S.W. Sam Jackson Park Road
Portland, OR 97201

(503) 494-7228

PENNSYLVANIA

CLINCAL NEUROPHYSIOLOLGY LABORATORY
CROZER-CHESTER MEDICAL CENTER
1 Medical Center Blvd.
Uplands, PA 19013

(215) 447-2911

PITTSBURGH

UNIVERSITY OF PITTSBURGH
School of Medicine
Dept. of Neurology
322 Scaife Hall
Pittsburgh, PA 15261

412-648-2024

RHODE ISLAND

ROGER WILLIAMS MEDICAL CENTER
Ambulatory Pavilion
50 Maude Street
Providence, R.I. 02908

401-456-2456

TENNESSEE

METHODIST HOSPITAL
One Crews
1265 Union Ave.
Memphis, TN 38104

901-726-8141

TEXAS

PRESBYTERIAN HOSPITAL OF DALLAS

Harry Knitter

8200 Walnut Hill Lane
Dallas, TX

THE UNIVERSITY OF TEXAS
HSC AT SAN ANTONIO
Division of Neurology
7703 Floyd Curl Drive
San Antonio, Texas

WASHINGTON

UNIVERSITY OF WASHINGTON
DIVISION OF NEUROLOGY
SEATTLE, WA 98195

WISCONSIN

ST. MARY'S HOPITAL
2320 NORTH LAKE DRIVE
MILWAUKEE, WI 53201

(414)291-1048

WISCONSIN PARKINSON ASSN.
945 N. 12th St.
Milwaukee, WI 53201

(414) 219-7450

V.A.HOSPITAL
1000 Locust Street
Reno, NV

(702) 328-1715

APPENDIX II

Reference Resources

The following are just some of the resources you'll find helpful in your search for pertinent information about PD:

AN ATLAS OF PARKINSON'S DISEASE AND RELATED DISORDERS,
G.D. Perkin
1998, $78.00

CARING FOR THE PARKINSON PATIENT: A PRACTICAL GUIDE,
J. Thomas Hutton et al
1999, $15.96

DEFENDING AGAINST THE ENEMY: Coping with Parkinson's Disease,
Eric R. Morgan
1997, $10.36

EAT WELL, STAY WELL WITH
PARKINSON'S DISEASE
Kathrynn Holder
1998, $19.95

SHAKING UP PARKINSON'S
Abe Lieberman
A current look at the disease that is
incapacitating over a million people
throughout the U.S. Recommended reading
by both patients and care parners.

LIVING WELL WITH PARKINSON'S
Glenn Wotton Atwood
PARKINSON'S DISEASE: A COMPLETE
GUIDE FOR PATIENTS AND FAMILIES
M.D. Weine, et al.

PARKINSON'S DISEASE: THE WAY
FORWARD!
An Integrated Approach, including Drugs,
Surgery. Neutrition, Bowel, and Muscle

Function, Self-Esteem, Sexuality and Stress Control – Geoffrey Leder, et al.

LIVING WELL WITH PARKINSON'S
Glenna Wotton Atwood

Other Kordene books by Harry Knitter:

HOLDING PATTERN:
AIRPORT WAITING MADE EASY
$9.95 PLUS $3.50 FOR SHIPPING AND HANDLING

WHY YOU SHOULD TAKE YOUR TRAVEL AGENT TO LUNCH $9.95 PLUS $3.50 FOR SHIPPING AND HANDLING

SIX YEARS TO SUNRISE
$15.00 PLUS $4.00 SHIPPING AND HANDLING

CALL 1-888-567-3363

Harry Knitter

So you have Parkinson's

...For heaven's sake, contact a good neurologist. Attend a support group or seminar meeting and ask the attendees who they work with. When one name comes up every time, book an appointment with that neurologist. Try to get a doctor who specializes in Parkinson's.

...Ask your doctor for a Handicapped hanger card for your car. It will save you many steps and make it easier for you to enter and leave your car.

...Check out your insurance options. You are going to need the very best coverage you can find. Look for special benefits in the medication area. Parkinson's medications are **very** expensive.

About the Author

"Harry Knitter is one of a growing number of PWP's (People with Parkinson's) who have fought back against the disease through surgery. This book chronicles his success with Deep Brain Stimulation of the sub-thalamic nucleus (DBS/STN). We have much in common, including the desire to make Parkinsonians aware of the reversible technique and to tell his story in a friendly, intimate way. What impressed me most was his message of hope and self-determination.

"The clear theme of this book and the work of the Parkinson Alliance is that those o f us who have a connection to Parkinson's are, for the most part, strong, resourceful, and optimistic. We eagerly look forward to a cure. But before we reach that glorious day, we need information. That's why we are conducting a survey which was formulated with invaluable input from Dr. Aleksandar Beric, member of Dr. Patrick Kelly's excellent

New York University Hospital surgical team. We invite you to participate in the survey if you have had bilateral STN more than six months ago.

The questionnaire identifies the issues that are so important to the Parkinson's community, including a Quality of Life assessment. It also asks about reliance on medication, exercise habits, changes in diet, alternative medication, and many other key points of a Parkinsonian's daily life.

"To obtain a copy of the survey form, contact us at The Parkinson Alliance, 211 College Rd.East, 3rd floor, Princeton, NJ 08540.

"In behalf of all Parkinson's patients, thank you for your input."

–Margaret Tuchman, President, The Parkinson's Alliance, and Board Member, Re-Wired for Life Foundation.